THE
AWESOME
ANCIENT
QUIZ BOOK

Horrible Histories:
The Savage Stone Age
The Awesome Egyptians
The Groovy Greeks
The Rotten Romans
The Cut-throat Celts
The Smashing Saxons
The Vicious Vikings
The Angry Aztecs
The Incredible Incas
The Measly Middle Ages
The Terrible Tudors
Even More Terrible Tudors
The Slimy Stuarts
The Gorgeous Georgians
The Vile Victorians
The Frightful First World War
The Woeful Second World War
The Blitzed Brits

Horrible Histories Specials:
Bloody Scotland
Cruel Kings and Mean Queens
Dark Knights and Dingy Castles
Ireland
Rowdy Revolutions
The 20th Century
Wicked Words

Also available:
Dreadful Diary
The Horribly Huge Quiz Book
Loathsome Letter-writing Pack
The Mad Millennium Play

Two-books-in-one:
The Groovy Greeks and The Rotten Romans
The Vicious Vikings and The Measly Middle Ages
The Terrible Tudors and The Slimy Stuarts
The Gorgeous Georgians and The Vile Victorians

THE
AWESOME
ANCIENT
QUIZ BOOK

TERRY DEARY   MARTIN BROWN

■SCHOLASTIC

Scholastic Children's Books,
Commonwealth House, 1–19 New Oxford Street,
London WC1A 1NU, UK

A division of Scholastic Ltd
London ~ New York ~ Toronto ~ Sydney ~ Auckland
Mexico City ~ New Delhi ~ Hong Kong

Published in the UK by Scholastic Ltd, 2001

Text copyright © Terry Deary, 2001
Illustrations copyright © Martin Brown, 1993–2001

ISBN 0 439 99231 1

All rights reserved
Typeset by M Rules
Printed by WS Bookwell, Finland

2 4 6 8 10 9 7 5 3 1

All rights reserved

CONTENTS

INTRODUCTION

Human beings are amazing! These feeble, ugly, hairy, two-legged creatures should have been wiped out millions of years ago – torn by tigers, drowned in deluges, poisoned by plagues, flattened by famines, scorched by sunshine or withered by wicked winters. Yet they've survived!

Humans have always used the one thing they have that other animals don't. Brainpower.

About 10,000 years ago they learned to work in teams and build villages, make farms and tame fire.

They spread across the face of the earth until they discovered the one hideously horrible thing that would stop them. Other human beings!

The most horrible things in human history are the stories of what people do to other people. Some are so hard to believe you ask yourself, 'Could people really be so cruel?'

Once we start to understand people then there is the chance that humans may survive another couple of million years. We may learn from the past and change the future. That's what history is about ... understanding people.

Never mind the dates. It's people and how they behave that counts. That's what you should be learning. So here's a book full of foul and fantastic facts about fellow humans who lived in distant times.

And because you are one of those ugly, hairy, two-legged human creatures you will also have that brilliant brain. So this book is written in a way that will exercise your brain – it doesn't just *tell* you the facts. It challenges you to work them out for yourself!

So, ugly, hairy, two-legged human creature – what are you waiting for?

ANCIENT TIMELINE

Ancient empires have risen and fallen throughout history like rockets at a party. As soon as one exploded brilliantly over the world it began to fall and another one was on its way up to dazzle us.

Unlike rockets, those ancient people did some pretty nasty things to make sure they succeeded on the way up – and on the way down they did some pretty nasty things to try and save themselves. But, just like rockets, they were always going to lose the battle in the end.

Before looking at the grim and gruesome empires, their rotten rulers and poor peoples, here's a very (very) rough idea of how the ancients rose and fell...

8000 BC Humans are farming, and settling into towns like Jericho in the Middle East, and starting to 'own' houses and animals and land. Oooops! That will lead to greed and fighting and killing just to 'own' someone else's things. Horrible History can really start now!

5500 BC Awesome Egyptian people begin to settle beside the Nile river. But they haven't invented the wheel yet – which is a bit of a drag!

5000 BC People begin to settle in Mesopotamia – a rich farming land in the Middle East (now called Iraq). Towns like Ur in southern Mesopotamia (Sumer) will grow into great cities.

3500 BC Sumerian people of Mesopotamia invent the wheel – which is a wheely good idea – and are using bronze-metal instead of stone tools.

3100 BC North and South Egypt unites under one king (or pharaoh). The start of a long line of rulers who will later build massive pyramids.

3000 BC Sumerian people invent writing around the same time as the Egyptians! Not only can we record history, we can have schools and history tests!

2650 BC First pyramids built in Egypt. You can see the point – it's there on the top.

2000 BC Ur city destroyed by Elamites (from south-west Iran) and that's pretty much the end of the Sumerians. The merciless Assyrians will take over Sumer.

1894 BC Mesopotamia ruled from the mighty city of Babylon now. But after Babylonian king Hammurabi dies in 1750 BC they'll struggle against the Assyrians and other invaders.

1600 BC Mycenaeans are the most powerful people in the place we call Greece. Their massive city walls were built by one-eyed giants – Cyclops. (Well that's what the Mycenaeans say!)

1550 BC Egypt switches to burying its kings in tombs cut into rock. Grave robbers were robbing those pyramids too easily.

1250 BC The Mycenaeans destroy Troy – legend says they used the famous wooden horse trick.

1200 BC Olmecs develop in Central America. Their ideas will teach the Mad Maya and the Angry Aztecs some curious things in years to come!

900 BC Savage Spartans set up a state in Greece. The Ancient Greeks will grow more powerful now.

776 BC The first Olympic games are held. Even the conquering Greeks need sport and fun.

753 BC The city of Rome is founded. This little city will rule the world one day.

671 BC Assyrians invade Egypt. You can't blame them. The Assyrians had defeated their neighbours but the Egyptians have been helping those neighbours to revolt!

539 BC The powerful Persians conquer Babylon then go on to take over Egypt. Persians become ancient top dogs.

356 BC Alexander the Great born in Macedonia – north of Greece. He will grow up to conquer Persia, Mesopotamia and Egypt as part of his plan to take over the world.

146 BC The Greeks are defeated by the Romans and become part of the last great ancient empire – the Roman Empire.

30 BC Egyptian queen Cleopatra kills herself and the Romans take over Egypt.

AD 286 Roman Empire too big to manage so the emperor splits it into east and West, each with its own emperor.

AD 400 The shaky Roman Empire starts to collapse as the barbarians attack from all sides.

MUDDY MESOPOTAMIA

Around 5000 BC some Stone Age hunters discovered that Mesopotamian mud grew great crops. So those early humans stopped wandering, hunting and gathering wild fruit and nuts. They stayed there and planted crops – hard work, but at least they didn't have to worry about where the next nut was going to come from.

The Mesopotamians started to build their shelters in groups and they formed the first villages. Then the groups grew larger and formed the first cities with the first kings. The people who built the world's first cities made them from mud bricks – muddy Mesopotamia.

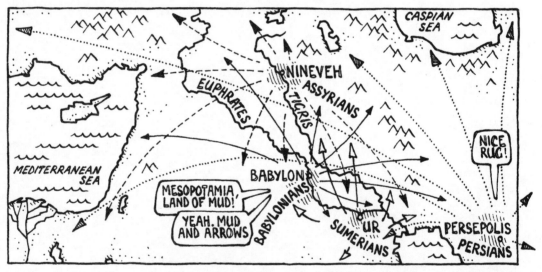

They invented the first writing … and you know what that means? Someone had to teach the writing skills – so they probably had the first teachers and the first schools! Muddy marvellous!

Marvellous Mesopotamians

Can you answer these muddy difficult questions? No? Well, look at the answers … then use them to test your teachers!

1 The first farmers needed to plough their land but oxen haven't been tamed to do this yet. What did they fasten the plough to?
a) their camel
b) their dog
c) their wife

2 In time, oxen are tamed and make great plough-pullers. What part of the oxen was the plough attached to?
a) its tail
b) its horns
c) its bum

3 What would a Mesopotamian king wear to make him look powerful and handsome?
a) a bronze crown with jewels to make him shine like the fairy on your Christmas tree
b) a pair of platform shoes to make him tall as a date-tree
c) a false beard and lots of eye make-up to make him look like something out of a pantomime

4 Early settlers to the north of Mesopotamia had very little wood for fires. What did they burn instead?
a) doggy droppings
b) seaweed
c) bones

5 How were seeds sown in the ploughed land?
a) using a device called a seed drill
b) thrown up in the air and scattered
c) pushed in one at a time by hand

6 Where would a Mesopotamian go for a quick meal?
a) a burger bar
b) a fried fish shop
c) a fried chicken shop

SUMERIAN SAUSAGE AND A BAG OF BABYLON BITS, PLEASE

7 What did the marvellous Mesopotamians invent to help their carts run smoothly?
a) the wheel
b) the sledge
c) the horse-drawn bus

8 Who probably invented the first wheel idea?
a) the first boy-racer on a chariot
b) the potters who wanted to turn their pots
c) children and their toy hoops

9 A Mesopotamian proverb said you should treat your mother like what?

a) a doormat
b) a goddess
c) a big cuddly teddy bear

CAN I HAVE A GLASS OF MILK, OH GREAT ONE?

10 We count in tens but the Sumerians of southern Mesopotamia counted in what?

a) 60s – which is why today we still have 60 minutes in an hour
b) sevens – which is why today we still have seven days in a week
c) 24s – which is why today we still have 24 hours in a day

Answers:

1c) The women and children pulled the first ploughs.

2b) In time, the 'yoke' was invented, so the ox shoulders took the strain.

3c) Men and women wore lots of make-up, especially around the eyes. (A woman would paste lead on her face so thick it was more like a mask.) They also had perfumed baths.

4c) They burned very slowly, but at least it meant nothing went to waste.

5a) Your teachers and school books will tell you the 'seed drill' was invented by a clever Englishman called Jethro Tull in the early 1700s. School books are wrong! Tull was 5,000 years behind the times. The Mesopotamians had funnels full of seed that trickled down a tube and followed the plough.

6b) There were lots of fish sellers in cities like Ur and some of them sold the fish already fried. Sadly, chips were not invented for another 5,000 years.

7a) The wheel was probably first used in Mesopotamia.

8b) Potters' wheels have been found from around 4500 BC but cart wheels came at least 250 years later.

9b) Another proverb said, 'A rich person can be happy, but someone with nothing can sleep peacefully at nights.' (Unless you can't afford a bed, of course.)

10a) And why we have 360 degrees in a circle (that's six times 60, you dummy).

Painful punishments

Mesopotamia was the first country with laws and the first to have policemen. We still have copies of the laws from a king called Hammurabi (1792–1750 BC).

There were some pretty tough laws in those days. If you knocked out someone's eye in a fight then *your* eye would be taken out … you can see the point, can't you? Same with teeth. A later law said this was 'An eye for an eye and a tooth for a tooth'. (Some people still believe in this sort of justice. Seems some things haven't changed much in 5,000 years!)

Here are ten Mesopotamian misdeeds and their painful punishments. Can you match them up?

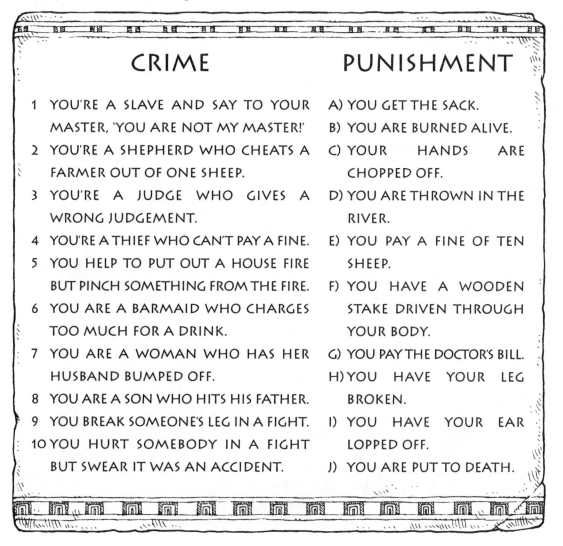

CRIME	PUNISHMENT
1 YOU'RE A SLAVE AND SAY TO YOUR MASTER, 'YOU ARE NOT MY MASTER!'	A) YOU GET THE SACK.
2 YOU'RE A SHEPHERD WHO CHEATS A FARMER OUT OF ONE SHEEP.	B) YOU ARE BURNED ALIVE.
3 YOU'RE A JUDGE WHO GIVES A WRONG JUDGEMENT.	C) YOUR HANDS ARE CHOPPED OFF.
4 YOU'RE A THIEF WHO CAN'T PAY A FINE.	D) YOU ARE THROWN IN THE RIVER.
5 YOU HELP TO PUT OUT A HOUSE FIRE BUT PINCH SOMETHING FROM THE FIRE.	E) YOU PAY A FINE OF TEN SHEEP.
6 YOU ARE A BARMAID WHO CHARGES TOO MUCH FOR A DRINK.	F) YOU HAVE A WOODEN STAKE DRIVEN THROUGH YOUR BODY.
7 YOU ARE A WOMAN WHO HAS HER HUSBAND BUMPED OFF.	G) YOU PAY THE DOCTOR'S BILL.
8 YOU ARE A SON WHO HITS HIS FATHER.	H) YOU HAVE YOUR LEG BROKEN.
9 YOU BREAK SOMEONE'S LEG IN A FIGHT.	I) YOU HAVE YOUR EAR LOPPED OFF.
10 YOU HURT SOMEBODY IN A FIGHT BUT SWEAR IT WAS AN ACCIDENT.	J) YOU ARE PUT TO DEATH.

Some laws were a bit unfair. Imagine you are a Mesopotamian boy. If your dad builds a house and it collapses and kills the owner, then your dad is executed. Fair enough? But if the house owner's *son* is killed, then *you* are killed!

And you had to be careful who you fought with. If you fought with a slave then you may get a small fine – but pick on a person posher than you and you'd be whipped in public!

Missing law

The Hammurabi laws are numbered 1–282 yet there are only 281 laws. Why?

a) Hammurabi couldn't count

b) There's no number 13 because it's unlucky

c) The lawmakers wrote one law twice

Answer:

b) Just like many, many people today, the Mesopotamians thought the number 13 was unlucky, so they skipped from law 12 to law 14. Wonder if they walked under ladders?

Nutty numbers

In 2001, a survey reported that most kids think maths teachers are fat, ugly, spotty nerds. (Now you know this isn't true … you know there are some thin maths teachers.) But we do not know what Mesopotamian kids thought of their maths teachers.

I WONDER WHAT THEY'LL BE LIKE THOUSANDS OF YEARS FROM NOW?

What we do know is that Mesopotamian numbers were pressed into wet clay with a blunt wooden 'pen'. Use modelling clay and an ice-lolly stick to copy these down…

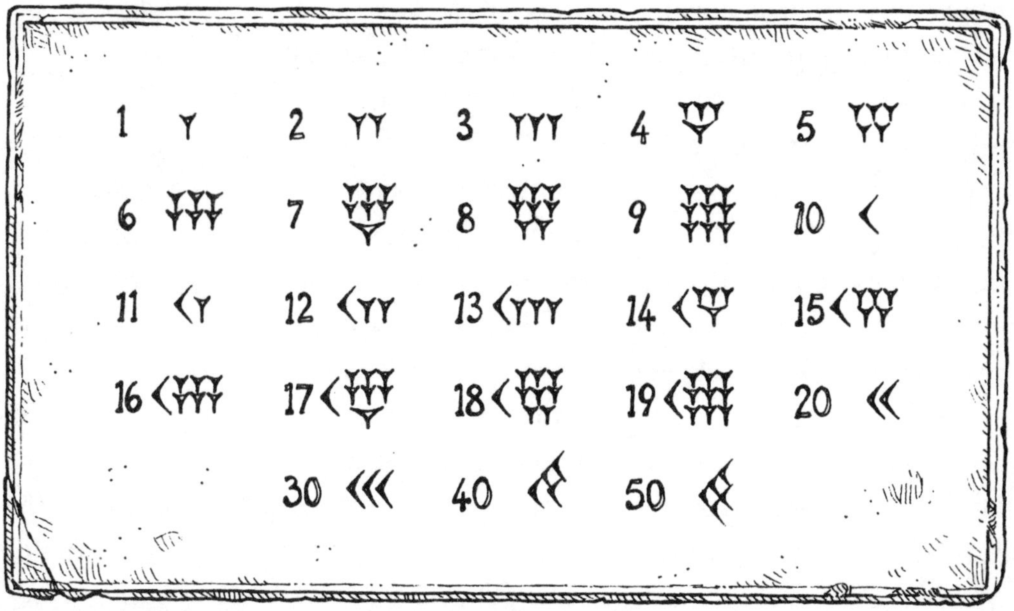

1	Y	2	YY	3	YYY	4	ᵞᵞ	5	ᵞᵞᵞ
6	YYY	7		8		9		10	⟨
11	⟨Y	12	⟨YY	13	⟨YYY	14	⟨ᵞᵞ	15	⟨ᵞᵞᵞ
16	⟨YYY	17		18		19		20	⟨⟨
		30	⟨⟨⟨	40		50			

Now try these Mesopotamian sums, using your Mesopotamian clay tablet, of course…

1 A Mesopotamian slave-owner had ⟨ slaves and cut Y ear off each of them. How many ears were left?

2 A Mesopotamian shepherd stole ᵞᵞᵞ sheep and had to pay back ⟨ sheep for every one stolen. How many did he pay back altogether?

3 A Mesopotamian king took ᐊ men into battle and ⟨ᵞᵞ were killed. How many men were left?

4 A doctor was paid ⟨⟨Y shekels for curing a wart and ⟨YYY shekels for curing a boil. How much did he earn altogether?

5 A farmer has YYY gan of land. He grows ⟨ gur of grain on each gan. How many gur does he grow altogether?

Answers:

1 ⟨⟨ − ⟨ = ⟨ ; 2 ᵞᵞᵞ × ⟨ = ᐊ ; 3 ᐊ − ⟨ᵞᵞ = ⟨⟨YYY

4 ⟨⟨Y + ⟨YYY = ⟨⟨⟨ᵞᵞᵞ ; 5 YYY × ⟨ = ⟨⟨⟨ .

Writing on the wall

Around 2000 BC the Assyrian people fought for their freedom from the Sumerians who ruled Mesopotamia. By 1000 BC they ruled a strong empire with their cruel and ruthless armies.

Ashurnasirpal ruled Assyria around 880 BC and faced many revolutions which he crushed ... cruelly and ruthlessly, of course. In 879 BC he had a 10-day-long party to celebrate the opening of his new palace in Nimrud and he invited 69,574 people.

Generous Ashurnasirpal? Not really. He wanted the guests to see the strength of his defences. The message was: Don't rebel against me.

And they would read on the walls of his palace a description of what he'd done to other rebels. The message was: Or else!

Of course a lot of these old writings get damaged over almost 3,000 years. Can you fit the words back in their right places on this stone tablet?

I TOOK ALL THE LEADING [1] AND HAD THEM [2] AND COVERED A PILLAR WITH THEIR [3]. SOME REBEL LEADERS WERE [4] INSIDE THE PILLARS, SOME WERE [5] ON [6] ON THE PILLAR, SOME WERE TIED TO STAKES AROUND THE BASE OF THE PILLAR. I SKINNED MANY IN MY COUNTRY AND SPREAD THEIR SKINS ON THE WALLS. I CUT OFF THE [7] AND [8] OF THE [9] OF THE [10]

And here are the missing words – but not in the right order!
spikes, revolt, skins, rebels, arms, buried alive, stuck, leaders, legs, skinned

Answers:
1 rebels; 2 skinned; 3 skins; 4 buried alive; 5 stuck; 6 spikes; 7 arms; 8 legs; 9 leaders; 10 revolt. He forgot to add: 'Have a nice nosh!'

Of course even the most ruthless rulers died in time. By 539 BC the Persians had conquered Mesopotamia. The people of the great city of Babylon tried to rebel in 482 BC – but had their mighty walls flattened and their temples destroyed. Bye-bye Mesopotamia, hello Persia!

Quick Mesopotamian quiz

Test your Mesopotamian general knowledge with this quick quiz…

1 What was a Mesopotamian man called Utnapishtim said to have built to save some people from a flood? (Clue: it worked so you can't say it was Noah good!)

2 In an ancient Mesopotamian legend the hero finds a plant that will give him everlasting youth. Which evil creature steals it from him? (Clue: *Boo! Hiss!*)

3 Around 2600 BC King Mes-kalam-dug died. What did his servants do to show how sorry they were? (Clue: they drank something that didn't agree with them.)

4 Around 2450 BC the King of Umma ripped up some Mesopotamian posts and started a war that lasted a hundred years. What was so important about these posts? (Clue: sounds like the posts were the Mesopotamians' front ear!)

5 In 2500 BC Mesopotamia began to collect slabs of clay. This was probably the world's first what? (Clue: you may find this book in one today!)

6 What tasty insect treat did the kings in the city of Mari enjoy around 1700 BC? (Clue: hop it!)

7 Mesopotamian fortune-tellers looked at sheep guts to see into the future. The guts were thrown on the ground. If it split at the stomach end it meant the king's son would rule; a split at the other end and a peasant would be the next king. But what if it split in the middle? That was bad news! Who would rule then? (Clue: you'd be crazy to let him rule you!)

8 By 1450 BC the Mittani people had taken over Mesopotamia. Fathers were strict with children and, if they were short of money, they would do something nasty. What would they do? (Clue: he'd shop the kids!)

9 In 879 BC the Assyrians invaded Mesopotamia and stopped the people of Babylon from worshipping the great god Marduk. How? (Clue: call the cops!)

10 Ashurbanipal the Assyrian took over Mesopotamia in 648 BC and was a pretty tough guy. Eight years later he defeated the Elamites and captured four of their princes. He took a chariot and made the four princes do what? (Clue: he didn't put the horse before the cart.)

Answers:

1 An ark. A flood really did kill thousands around the year 2800 BC. The survivors told the story of an ark that was built to save people, just as in the Bible story of Noah. They believed that the angry gods flooded the earth because the noisy humans were giving them a headache! So now you know ... stop that row or it will rain for 40 days and 40 nights!

2 A serpent. Again, just like the Bible story of the evil serpent that spoiled everything for Adam and Eve. The serpent in the story of Mesopotamian king Gilgamesh nicks the plant. The lesson seems to be, never trust a snake.

3 They drank poison and died. It was probably a great honour to be buried with your king in Mesopotamia. Then you could hop off with him to the afterlife and serve him there! Great idea! It means you are sure of a job when you get to heaven and you don't have to join a heavenly dole queue!

4 The posts marked the border of Mesopotamia and Umma. Mesopotamian king Mesalim put the posts in to say, 'This is the frontier – you stay on that side. OK?' The King of Umma ripped up the posts to show he disagreed. People were still dying a hundred years later in the war that followed.

5 First library. There were all sorts of books including proverbs that still make sense today. 'You may be afraid of your master, you may be afraid of your king, but the one you should really fear is the tax collector!' Nothing changes.

6 Grasshoppers. That should've made them feel chirpy. The grasshoppers were stuck through with a thin skewer of wood … you need to know this if you'd like to serve them at your next birthday party. The Mari kings also enjoyed ostrich eggs in the world's biggest omelette.

7 A madman. Want to try this sheep-gut fortune-telling? Well, sausages are just animal guts, aren't they? Pop some in a pan and see where they split! If your animal-guts sausage splits in the middle you'll be ruled by a mad teacher – nothing new there then.

8 Sell their children. Fathers were the head of the house and could whip disobedient children, chain them to a wall or shut them up in a dark cave (probably with spiders!). And they were kind men compared to the ones over the border in Assyria. In Assyria a man could not only  beat his wife but punish her by cutting off her ears or her nose. If a husband died, the wife was ruled by her sons. A foul fate for females.

9 The Assyrians pinched the statue of Marduk and the Babylonians were lost without it – imagine your local football team losing their lucky mascot! The awful Assyrians also took soil from Mesopotamia and scattered it in Assyrian city streets – so that the people of Assyria could feel good about trampling over enemy soil.

10 He put the four princes in front of the chariot and made them pull him through his capital city, Nineveh, while the people cheered him. Sounds like a good punishment for school bullies – make them pull the school bus!

THE AWESOME EGYPTIANS

Around 5000 BC the Awesome Egyptians moved into the land by the River Nile. Every year the river flooded and left lovely squidgy mud covering

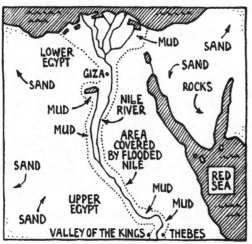

the fields for a few miles on either side – lovely squidgy mud that was good for growing crops. Sound familiar?

The people of the Nile could usually grow enough food to live – but they were always worried that one year the Nile would let them down and they'd all starve. So they invented gods and prayed that the gods would make the Nile flood.

Then along came some really clever people who said, 'Actually, we are those gods you pray to! So give us lots of food, build us palaces, worship us and we'll look after you!' These really clever people became known as 'pharaohs' – probably because they had a 'fair-old' life with peasants slaving for them![1]

Some historians reckon the Pharaohs came from where?

a) They were chiefs of villages who conquered other villages till they had a kingdom.

b) They were invaders from another country who defeated the Egyptians and ruled them.

c) They were spacemen who landed, defeated the Egyptians and ruled the peasants.

1 Actually, 'Pharaoh' is the Egyptian word for 'Great House'. The peasants didn't dare to speak the name of their king so they called him 'The Great House' – a bit like a Brit calling the queen, 'Mrs Buckingham Palace' or an American calling the president 'Mr White House'.

Phunny pharaohs

The Egyptian kings, or pharaohs, ruled for almost 3,000 years so there were bound to be a few odd ones among all that lot. If there had been newspapers around in those days then imagine the headlines – but there weren't and if there had been they'd have been a bit crumbly by now and key words may have fallen out. Can you replace them?

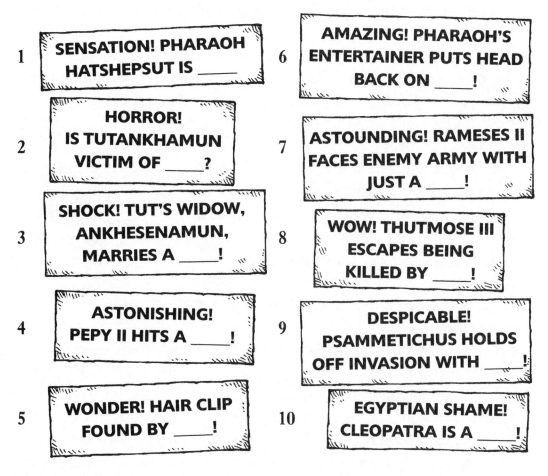

1 SENSATION! PHARAOH HATSHEPSUT IS _____

2 HORROR! IS TUTANKHAMUN VICTIM OF _____ ?

3 SHOCK! TUT'S WIDOW, ANKHESENAMUN, MARRIES A _____ !

4 ASTONISHING! PEPY II HITS A _____ !

5 WONDER! HAIR CLIP FOUND BY _____ !

6 AMAZING! PHARAOH'S ENTERTAINER PUTS HEAD BACK ON _____ !

7 ASTOUNDING! RAMESES II FACES ENEMY ARMY WITH JUST A _____ !

8 WOW! THUTMOSE III ESCAPES BEING KILLED BY _____ !

9 DESPICABLE! PSAMMETICHUS HOLDS OFF INVASION WITH _____ !

10 EGYPTIAN SHAME! CLEOPATRA IS A _____ !

Clue: The following words fit the gaps – but where?
Greek, hundred, money, goose, murderer, elephants, magician, lion, woman, wrinkly.

23

Answers:

1 Woman. Hatshepsut wore a chin wig so she looked like a man. She was a good pharaoh but later kings were shocked at the thought of a woman ruler. They hacked her name off her monuments so they could pretend she never existed. But she did.

2 Murderer. Some people believe the young pharaoh was murdered by his own advisor, Ay, who went on to take the throne.

3 Wrinkly. After Tutankhamun was dead, the best way for the ageing Ay to get the throne was to marry Tut's widow, Ankhesenamun. She tried to run off with a foreign prince but he died. In the end she was forced to marry the old man.

4 Hundred. Pepy II ruled from the age of 6 till he was a hundred years old. Did he get a telegram from the queen?

5 Magician. Pharaoh Sneferu's wife lost her hair clip in a lake as she rowed across it. Sneferu ordered his court magician to find it. It was reported that the magician folded the lake in half and walked across to the clip. Oh, yeah? And there are fairies at the bottom of my garden.

6 Goose. The pharaohs had all sorts of court entertainers. The one who appeared to remove the heads of geese and put them back on was obviously a clever trickster. But could he do anything with your Christmas turkey?

WHY COULDN'T HE PULL ME OUT OF A HAT LIKE OTHER MAGICIANS

7 Lion. Rameses faced the Hittite enemy army with his pet lion. Then his friends turned up and attacked the Hittites from behind. Rameses (and the lion) were saved.

8 Elephants. Thutmose III was a great Pharaoh who conquered all of Egypt's enemies. But, on the way, he had a few close shaves with death. In Syria he was almost trampled to death by a herd of wild elephants.

9 Money. By 630 BC Egypt was past its greatest years. Enemies weren't defeated, they were bribed. And, big mistake, the Greeks are paid to come to Egypt to help with the fighting. A bit like inviting a fox into your hen-house.

10 Greek. Cleopatra is probably the most famous Egyptian queen … except she wasn't. She ruled after Egypt was conquered by the Greeks.

Potty pyramids

They are H-U-G-E. The pyramids were built as graves for the pharaohs after they left this life. They were filled with goodies so the kings would be as rich in the next life as they were in this life.

Of course they've all been robbed now – some were robbed at the time of the burial and the rest have been cleaned out by greedy treasure hunters in the twentieth century. (They said they were collecting historical material for our education. That's a bit like a bank robber saying his hobby is collecting bank notes … they are all just robbers!)

Not everyone agrees the pyramids are graves, of course. Thinking about those great lumps of dense stone, are people with great lumps of dense brain who have other ideas. But which of the following wacky ideas have some people seriously believed? Answer true or false…

Someone has said that the pyramids are …

1 Adverts. The priests wanted to leave something to show the world how great they were.
2 Simple landmarks. All maps would be drawn with the pyramids at the centre and distances worked out from there.
3 Chambers of horrors. Dead kings were stuck inside, then the Egyptian people were charged two onions an hour to walk around and view their kingly corpses.
4 Sundials. The shadow from the Great Pyramid would be used to work out the time.
5 Fortune-telling machines. They've been used to predict the birth of Christ, the date of World War I and the end of the world – AD 2979 if you're worried.
6 Star calculators. They help to measure the speed of light, the distances from the earth to the sun and to keep a record of the movement of the stars.

7 Calendars. They can measure the length of a year to three decimal places.

8 Star maps. The pyramids are laid out in the same pattern as a cluster of stars called Orion. Of course you could only see this pattern if you are ten miles up in the air – or a Martian in a flying saucer.

9 Centres of invisible forces of the universe. Weird things can happen there – like blunt razors turning sharp and people feeling wobbly at the knees when they enter.

10 Maths calculators. Take the distances around the edges and the angles and whatnot and you can work out the distance round a circle (its circumference) if you know the distance across (its diameter).

> *Answer:*
> All except 3 have been believed by someone … usually someone with more thumbnail than brain, but you can believe them if you like. Most people just admit they are huge tombs for dead kings.

Mad mummies

Egyptians believed that one day the world would end. When it did everyone who had a body would move on to a wonderful afterlife. But if your body had rotted, you would miss out on this treat. So it was the Egyptians' duty to make sure their dead pharaohs didn't rot. They turned them into mummies. Could *you* make a mummy? Here's what you do … unfortunately the instructions have been scrambled by a mummy's curse. Can you rearrange them?

a) Rip open the front of the body and take out the liver, the stomach, the intestines and the lungs – but leave the heart inside.

b) Throw the brain away and pack the skull with 'natron' – a sort of salt that stops bodies rotting.

c) Stuff the empty body with rags to give it the right shape, then sew it up.

d) Take the body to a 'beautiful house' – that's an open-ended tent in the open air – so the disgusting smells are blown away!

e) Wash the liver, the stomach, the intestines and the lungs in wine and place them in their own sealed jars – canopic jars.

f) Put the body on a wooden table with bars of wood (not a solid top) so you can reach underneath to bandage it.

g) Perform the ceremony of the 'Opening of the mouth' – or the mummy won't be able to eat, drink or speak in the next life.

h) Soak the body in natron for 70 days till it is well pickled.

i) Wrap the body in bandages from head to foot.

j) Remove the brain by pushing a chisel up the nose to break through, then hook the brain out with a piece of wire.

Answer: d), f), j), b), a), e), h), c), i), g).

Get it right? Now make a mask that looks like the pharaoh did when he was alive and cover it with gold. Pop him in a stone coffin, stick him in his pyramid and have a party. Everyone invited … except the mummy, of course. You are now an expert mummifier, or 'embalmer' (to use a more technical term). You can now go out and practise on a favourite dead teacher if you like!

Mummy magic

Of course, desert-dry Egyptian summers dry up and preserve bodies anyway. An ancient peasant was buried in the desert sands and his body dried up but didn't rot. He's in the British Museum today and the keepers have given him a nickname. What is it?

The following mummies will tell you a bit of mummy magic. But some of them are not telling the truth. Take the liars away and the ones that are left will spell out the peasant's nickname.

Answers:

G – Yes. Bits often fell off bodies and embalmers would replace the missing bits with a ball of linen or a piece of wood.

I – Yes. In Victorian times people flocked to Dr Pettigrew's unwrappings. They were a sell-out like today's pop concerts. At one the Archbishop of Canterbury was turned away because the hall was full.

O – No. Dr Pettigrew's work was so popular that the Duke of Hamilton asked to be mummified – after his death, of course. Pettigrew mummified him in 1852 and the daft duke was buried, like a pharaoh, in a stone coffin.

N – Yes. The spells were there to protect the mummy in its dangerous journey to the afterlife.

U – No. The 'Books of the Dead' were prayers against evil spirits and *not* curses. The 'mummy's curse' idea is nineteenth-century nonsense and twentieth-century tosh!

T – No. Once the mummy reaches the afterlife his heart will be weighed in scales. If the heart is heavy with wickedness then he will be eaten by 'The Devourer' – a monster that is part crocodile, part hippopotamus and part lion.

G – Yes. Mummies had boiling lakes and rivers of fire to cross before they reached their afterlife. There was also a snake that spat poison at them. The mummies needed their 'Book of the Dead' to ward off evil.

Y – No. Sometimes eyes were replaced with black stones … though Rameses IV was given two little onions!

E – Yes. The Victorians bought and sold bits of mummy to decorate their houses! A mummy foot or hand in a glass case was quite common.

R – Yes. Dug-up mummies became so common 200 years ago that they were thrown into ovens and used as fuel so the poor people could eat.

You should end up with the word GINGER – the mummy's nickname. The museum keepers called him that because he had red-brown hair.

But … there is a story that 'Ginger' wasn't an ancient Egyptian mummy after all. The British Museum collectors were tricked. They went to Egypt looking for mummies and a crooked dealer sold the Brits a fairly new corpse that he'd dried out! There is even a story that the dealer sold them the corpse of … his brother!

Murderous mummy quiz

See if you can pick the right answers to these murderous questions…

1 The Arabs were the first to uncover ancient mummies. They thought the bodies were wrapped in something they called 'mumi', a sticky black stuff that goes hard. We wouldn't call this stuff 'mumi', we'd call it what?

a) bandages
b) tar
c) toffee

2 In 1375 BC King Akhenaten argued with his daughter and sent her for execution. What spiteful thing did he have done to her corpse?

a) He cut off her hair so her family couldn't admire her beauty any more.
b) He cut off a hand so she couldn't go into the afterlife.
c) He cut off a finger to get a ring back.

3 The famous Mummy of Tutankhamun was dug up when?

a) 1822
b) 1872
c) 1922

4 In ancient Egyptian times the punishment for robbing a grave was what?

a) horrible torture

b) horrible execution

c) horrible torture followed by horrible execution

5 A pharaoh's mother could be given a rich burial too. The mother of Cheops had a burial shaft dug so deep no one could rob her coffin. Yet they did. How?

a) They dug a tunnel through the rock to reach the coffin.

b) They hijacked the coffin on its way to the burial shaft.

c) They pinched the valuables before she was buried.

6 How did the Egyptians carry the huge pyramid stones from the Nile?

a) on huge, eight-wheeled carts pulled by camels

b) on wooden sledges

c) with the help of special cranes

7 A grave robber reached into a coffin to steal some gold. The lid fell and trapped him, then the roof fell in and killed him. He was found later, skeleton hand still trapped in the coffin. How many years was his corpse there?

a) 26 years

b) 260 years

c) 2600 years

8 The peasants who built the pyramids weren't slaves (whatever schoolbooks say!). They were paid in food and clothing. What did workers do who were not paid on time?

a) They went on strike until they were paid.

b) They went on strike until they were executed by the army.

c) They went home and left the pyramid unfinished.

9 An 1880s tomb-robber was caught after selling tomb treasures of 30 mummies. What did the Egyptians do with the robber?

a) gave him a reward for finding the mummies

b) cut off his hands

c) cut off his head

10 What have archaeologists learnt from mummy's teeth?
a) The ancient Egyptians used toothpaste.
b) The ancient Egyptians ate beef burgers.
c) Egyptian bread was coarse and gritty.

Answers:

1b) Tar. Mumi was the Arabic word for tar. Of course the Arabs were wrong – they weren't tar, but the name 'mumi' has stuck … like tar!

2b) Only a complete body could pass into the afterlife so the kruel king was trying to prevent her enjoying Egyptian heaven!

3c) It was found by archaeologist, Howard Carter, in a burial chamber (not a pyramid).

4c) But this didn't stop the robbers. Their favourite trick was to bribe the tomb-makers and the guards to make the robbery easier. Sometimes the pharaoh's own priests helped in the robbery!

5c) Modern archaeologists dug up the coffin of Cheops's mother, Hetepheres. It had not been disturbed, yet there were just two poor silver bracelets with the skeleton. Where was the fabulous treasure Cheops said he'd buried with her? Nicked before the coffin was sealed. Cheops's Prime Minister, Yussef, is the chief suspect.

6b) The early Egyptians didn't have carts because they hadn't invented the wheel. They used peasants to drag the stones from the river to the pyramid building site. And one stone weighed about as much as three family cars would today!

7a) The robber was trapped in the tomb and his greedy skeleton was found by archaeologists in 1970. They knew when he had died because in the skeleton's tattered coat was a newspaper – dated 1944.

8a) The first strike in history was at a pyramid. The workers sat down on the shady side of the pyramid and refused to lift another stone. They were paid.

9a) The robber was rewarded for finding the mummies – which he hadn't touched. The Egyptian government 'forgot' about the loot he'd stolen and gave him a job ... as a guide, showing tourists round the tombs.

10c) The teeth are badly worn down from eating bread. The corn was ground between stones. But grit from the stones got into the flour. Eating bread must have been like eating sandpaper. Yeuch!

Curious curses

Mummies are a bit creepy. Looking at corpses of long-dead people is enough to give you goosebumps on your goose-bumps. But it's not creepy enough for some people! They have to imagine the mummies aren't just shrivelled flesh – they have to believe the mummy spirits wander around.

These spirits bring curses and spells to the living people who disturbed their rest and robbed their graves! Most of these stories are nonsense. But what about this one...

A mummified priestess was dug up in Egypt and brought to England:

- Douglas Murray was the man who dug her mummy up in 1910. Soon after, he had a hunting accident in which his gun exploded. He had to have an arm amputated.
- His two expedition friends died and so did the servants who went on his archaeological trip.
- He gave one of the grave jewels to a woman friend – but her mother died soon after, her fiancée left her and she fell ill.
- Murray offered the mummy to a London museum where a photographer took pictures of the mummy – then dropped dead. A wagon-driver was crushed when the mummy's stone case fell off the wagon and pinned him against a wall. A museum caretaker also died.
- The mummified priestess was then sold to America. It was loaded on to a ship and kept just behind the control room – the bridge. It is said that the mummy's curse affected the captain's judgement. It made him steer the ship into an iceberg and sink. The ship was the *Titanic*.

BUT ... there is no written evidence that the *Titanic* was carrying a mummy. Believers say, 'The Captain didn't record the mummy cargo because he didn't want to frighten the passengers.'

Still, there are some juicy stories about mummy curses. Here is the most famous – the Curse of Tutankhamun's Tomb. *Horrible Histories* have looked into the truth behind the stories. Each of the following 10 stories has been told by someone at some time. Can you work out  which stories are simply LIES, which are MISTAKES and which are TRUE but can be explained?

1 The Earl of Carnarvon paid for the expedition to dig up the mummy of Tutankhamun and he died within six months of the discovery.

2 Arthur Mace was one of the first to enter the tomb and he died shortly after.

3 When Tutankhamun's mummy was unwrapped the archaeologists found a curse wrapped in the bandages. It said: 'They who enter this sacred tomb shall swiftly be visited by the wings of death.'

4 Lord Carnarvon pricked his cheek on a poisoned arrowhead in the tomb and died from its poisoning.

5 When Lord Carnarvon died his favourite dog howled at the exact moment of his death. The dog was 3,000 miles away in England.

6 Lord Carnarvon's friend, Count Hamon, owned an ancient mummy's hand. It was as soft and fresh as the day it was cut off the mummy.

7 Mohammed Ibrahim had been very much against moving Tutankhamun's treasures to France in 1966. He fought to keep the mummy in Egypt. But he lost the fight in a final meeting. Ibrahim left the meeting ... and walked into the path of a taxi. He died instantly.

8 A worker in the British Museum was fastening labels to things stolen from Tutankhamun's tomb. He dropped dead.

9 American Millionaire George Gould visited the tomb. He was fine before he went but died soon after.

10 The mummy's 'curse' is in fact ancient Egyptian germs that were sealed into the tomb 3,000 years ago.

Answers:

1 True, but... Carnarvon was a sickly man. He'd been in a car accident a while before the mummy-discovery and was not fit enough to cope with the heat of Egypt.

2 True, but... Mace had been ill before he entered the tomb. He had pleurisy. There were no cures for this illness in 1922.

3 Lies. A newspaper reported this curse soon after Carnarvon's death. The mummies were buried with a 'Book of the Dead' in their coffins. Some people believe this book cursed grave robbers. The truth is the 'Book of the Dead' was a collection of prayers and charms to protect the mummy spirit in its next life. It is not a book of curses.

4 Mistake. Lord Carnarvon got a mosquito bite on his face – not a poison-arrow scratch. He cut it open when he was shaving and that gave him blood-poisoning and a fever. He was very weak and caught a lung infection. That's what killed him, not the scratch on the face.

5 True, but... It's a creepy story told by Lord Carnarvon's son. But what has that to do with a mummy's curse?

6 Lies. Hamon was given a mummy hand but it was a very dead one. Hamon made a lot of money being a fortune-teller, so it suited him to tell stories about ghostly experiences.

7 True, but... He was a 'friend' of the mummy, trying to keep it in Egypt. Surely the curse would only affect enemies of the mummy?

8 Lies. The British Museum never had any objects from Tut's tomb.

9 Mistake. Gould was not in good health before his visit. He went to Egypt because he was ill, but the stress of the travelling killed him.

10 Mistake. The air in the tomb wouldn't be very healthy, but King Tut's germs wouldn't kill a visitor today.

Rotten religion

The trouble with Egyptian gods is that they are a bit mixed up. Their stories were repeated for 3,000 years and they were never the same. So you get odd things. The Sun god, Re, became mixed with Amun (the god of Thebes City) and by around 1500 BC became one god … Amun-Re. And moon-god Thoth sometimes appears as an ibis bird and sometimes as a baboon!

Now see if you can match the god to the story. (There are clues in brackets – as if an awesome Egyptian expert like you would need them!)

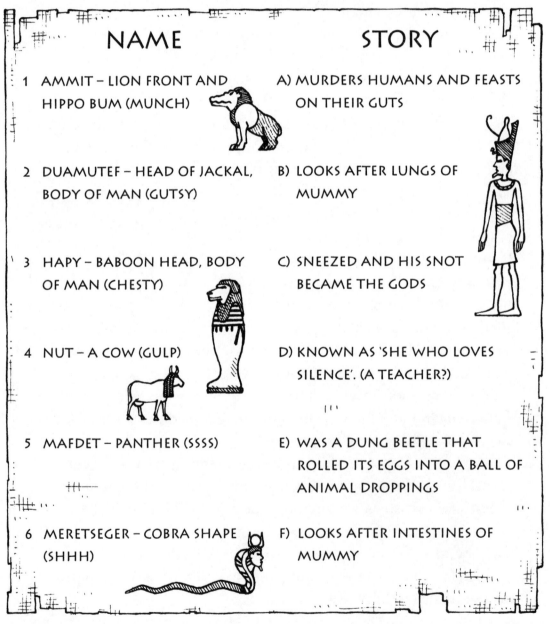

NAME

1 AMMIT – LION FRONT AND HIPPO BUM (MUNCH)

2 DUAMUTEF – HEAD OF JACKAL, BODY OF MAN (GUTSY)

3 HAPY – BABOON HEAD, BODY OF MAN (CHESTY)

4 NUT – A COW (GULP)

5 MAFDET – PANTHER (SSSS)

6 MERETSEGER – COBRA SHAPE (SHHH)

STORY

A) MURDERS HUMANS AND FEASTS ON THEIR GUTS

B) LOOKS AFTER LUNGS OF MUMMY

C) SNEEZED AND HIS SNOT BECAME THE GODS

D) KNOWN AS 'SHE WHO LOVES SILENCE'. (A TEACHER?)

E) WAS A DUNG BEETLE THAT ROLLED ITS EGGS INTO A BALL OF ANIMAL DROPPINGS

F) LOOKS AFTER INTESTINES OF MUMMY

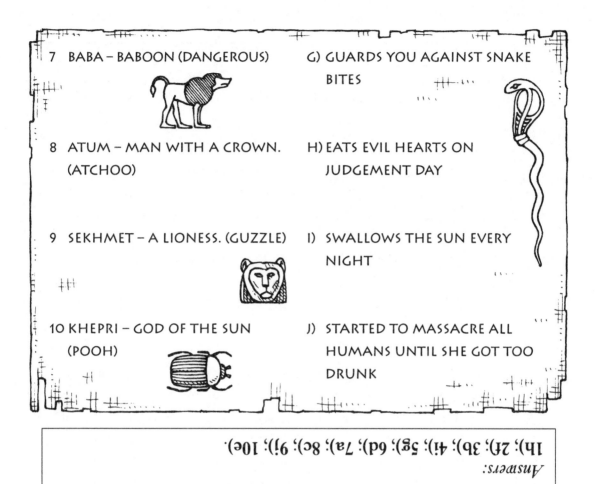

7 BABA – BABOON (DANGEROUS)

G) GUARDS YOU AGAINST SNAKE BITES

8 ATUM – MAN WITH A CROWN. (ATCHOO)

H) EATS EVIL HEARTS ON JUDGEMENT DAY

9 SEKHMET – A LIONESS. (GUZZLE)

I) SWALLOWS THE SUN EVERY NIGHT

10 KHEPRI – GOD OF THE SUN (POOH)

J) STARTED TO MASSACRE ALL HUMANS UNTIL SHE GOT TOO DRUNK

Answers:
1h); 2f); 3b); 4i); 5g); 6d); 7a); 8c); 9j); 10e).

Gruesome gods

Most awesome Egyptian myths have various versions of the same story. Here is one version of the Isis and Osiris story. Sadly our suffering scribe has scrambled the terrible tale in places! Can you unscramble the words in capitals? (It's easy – about as easy as unscrambling a scrambled egg!)

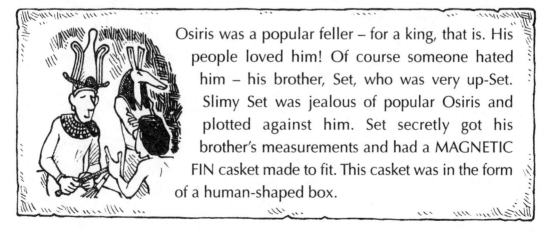

Osiris was a popular feller – for a king, that is. His people loved him! Of course someone hated him – his brother, Set, who was very up-Set. Slimy Set was jealous of popular Osiris and plotted against him. Set secretly got his brother's measurements and had a MAGNETIC FIN casket made to fit. This casket was in the form of a human-shaped box.

Sneaky Set then IN DOG'S EAR a large feast. Seedy Set invited Osiris and 72 others. At the height of the IF IT IS STEVE Set produced the casket and ACNE DO NUN that it would be given to whoever it fitted. All the guests tried the casket for size, but none fitted until finally Osiris stepped into the casket. (What a mug!)

Set (who was not a mug) immediately slammed the lid closed and sealed the casket shut (with boiling lead). The SAD LEE coffin was then thrown into the Nile.

Isis was upset at the loss of her husband and SHE CARED for the casket all over Egypt. At last she found it where it had come to rest in the roots of a huge tree.

Isis took the coffin back for a proper ALI RUB. For safety she hid it in the marshes beside the Nile. Unfortunately for Isis, Set found the casket while he was out hunting and was so ENRAGED he chopped the body of Osiris into pieces, and RESTED CAT the parts throughout the land of Egypt.

Poor Isis had to then set out again looking for the bits of her husband. At last she found all the parts except one (his naughty bit) and SMEARS BLEED Osiris and wrapped him in bandages. The first mummy!

He was also a daddy and his son, Horus, went out to battle his savage uncle Set. After a series of battles neither was able to win. In the end Osiris was made king of the underworld, Horus king of the living, and Set ruler of the deserts as the god of evil. So they all died happy ever after!

Answers:

These are the unscrabbled words in the correct order: magnificent; organised; festivities; announced; sealed; searched; burial; angered (or enraged!); scattered; reassembled.

Killing ... and curing

Egyptian doctors treated people with a mixture of medicine and magic. Some may have cured, but some may have killed. Look at some of the Egyptian beliefs about death and doctoring and make up your own mind.

1 A peasant like you could become a god. Gods were usually dead kings. But ordinary people could become gods too if they died in a certain way. How did they have to die?
a) by falling off a pyramid
b) by saving a pharaoh in battle
c) by drowning in the Nile

2 The Egyptians used clever cures such as onion juice (an antibiotic) but also some horrible ones. In some medical scrolls the Egyptians described how you could make medicine using 19 different types of what?
a) pee
b) poo
c) plum

3 In the 1920s some English people thought they were using an ancient Egyptian cure for children who wet the bed. The child had to eat what?
a) a cooked mouse
b) a cooked louse
c) a crooked house

4 The Egyptian cure for burns was to cover them completely in ... what?
a) jam
b) honey
c) money

5 Modern doctors think the Egyptians may have been able to help people see better at night. What did they use?
a) blood from a white cat's tail
b) juice from an ox's liver
c) pee from a greyhound

Answers:

1c) The River Nile was the most important thing in Egypt. Without its flooding there would just be a desert and no great nation. So the river became holy. And from around 1550 BC anyone who drowned in the River Nile could become a god and have their own little temple! So, you want to become an Egyptian god? Go take a long walk off a short plank over the Nile!

2b) Medicines were made from all sorts of poo, including fly and ostrich droppings .

3a) In Egypt the bones of the mouse were *not* eaten but wrapped in a cloth and the cloth hung round the neck of the child.

4b) Honey was put on the wound and probably worked in a lot of cases. Like onion juice, it is an antibiotic, so the Egyptians made a lucky guess. But they also believed that evil spirits hate honey and would be driven off by it (not such a good guess).

5b) Animal liver is high in vitamin A and could help some types of night-blindness.

Super scribes

The best job in Egypt was being a scribe. Who said so? The scribes! Their job was to write things down. They reckoned people like reed-cutters

were eaten by mosquitoes and farmers just worked themselves to death. The scribe was his own boss, made lots of money and paid no taxes! What a life!

Trainee scribes spent seven years in scribe school, copying the teacher's writing the way you copy off a blackboard.

A young scribe would…

- make his own pen by chewing the end of a reed to make a sort of paintbrush
- carry a few different sizes of brush-pens by sticking them behind his ear
- use black 'ink' that was a block of soot and gum, or red-soil for red ink

He'd use the blocks of ink the way a modern painter uses watercolours.

Got your reed? Chewed the end? Then you're ready to begin your training. Here are a few foul Egyptian facts for you to copy – but first you have to fit in the missing words.

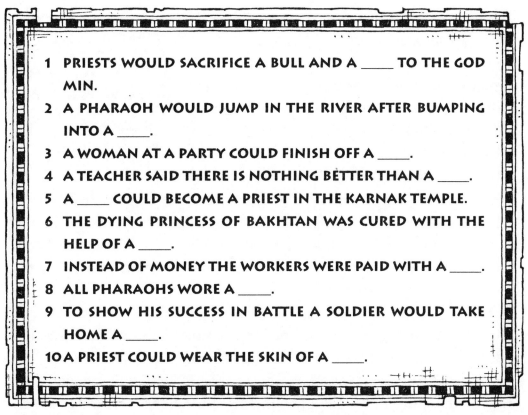

1 PRIESTS WOULD SACRIFICE A BULL AND A ____ TO THE GOD MIN.

2 A PHARAOH WOULD JUMP IN THE RIVER AFTER BUMPING INTO A ____.

3 A WOMAN AT A PARTY COULD FINISH OFF A ____.

4 A TEACHER SAID THERE IS NOTHING BETTER THAN A ____.

5 A ____ COULD BECOME A PRIEST IN THE KARNAK TEMPLE.

6 THE DYING PRINCESS OF BAKHTAN WAS CURED WITH THE HELP OF A ____.

7 INSTEAD OF MONEY THE WORKERS WERE PAID WITH A ____.

8 ALL PHARAOHS WORE A ____.

9 TO SHOW HIS SUCCESS IN BATTLE A SOLDIER WOULD TAKE HOME A ____.

10 A PRIEST COULD WEAR THE SKIN OF A ____.

Missing words: statue, book, pig, severed hand, bag of corn, leopard, wooden beard, lettuce, woman, barrel of bee.

Answers:

1 Lettuce. At the harvest festival the priests offered a holy bull some corn. If it ate it, that was a good sign – but not for the bull. The bull was slaughtered and eaten! The priests also offered a holy lettuce to the God Min! Lettuce was supposed to act like a love potion – so offer some to that girl/boy you fancy and see if it works!

2 Pig. Pigs were thought to be unclean. Anyone who accidentally touched one was supposed to run to the nearest river and throw him/herself in – clothes and all! Swineherds were not allowed into temples. That is sow unfair! (Some historians think the ancient Greeks who reported this may have got it a bit wrong, because the Egyptians ate lots of pork.)

3 Barrel of beer. Egyptian women drank as much as the men at parties. You had to drink your host's beer till you were drunk. In fact it was an insult *not* to get drunk. In a tomb painting a woman announces, 'I want to drink till I'm pickled. My guts are as dry as straw!' Charming lady!

4 Book. The scribes were important people in Egypt and their teachers could be really top people. Teachers wrote 'The Wisdom of Duauf' which had lots of wise sayings. One of the sayings was: 'Learn to love books – there is nothing better than books!' Three thousand years later teachers are *still* saying that! (Or it could simply be that your teachers are three thousand years old?)

5 Woman. Usually women were not allowed to be priests – a bit like the Christian church until the end of the twentieth century! But around 1000 BC one of the pharaoh's daughters became a priest.

6 Statue. The pharaoh's sister-in-law was ill and her family begged him to send the statue of the Egyptian moon-god, Khonsu. He did and she was cured. Remember that next time you pig out on too much chocolate cake and become ill. All you need is a statue!

7 Bag of corn. And in the reign of Rameses III the workers didn't get their corn on time. They went on strike – the first strike in history. Corny but true.

8 Wooden beard. Of course the pharaoh was the number one priest – and priests had no hair. But the king had to show he was really grown-up by having a beard. How do you have a beard if you have no hair? Wear a false one, made of wood or woven plant fibre. It was hung on wires from a band around his brow. When he died he swapped it for a godly beard – one that is plaited and turned up at the ends. Very fashionable in heaven, of course.

9 Severed hand. Egyptian soldiers chopped off the right hands of dead enemies. This allowed the pharaohs to count the number of dead.

Sometimes they cut off the enemy's naughty bits and Egyptian war paintings often show piles of these stacked up!

10 Leopard. Usually priests would wear no animal clothes at all – no leather sandals or belts. But the skin of a leopard (or a cheetah) was worn by the chief priest. It was worn like a cloak with the head of the animal hanging over his right shoulder. Grr-reat idea.

Wrotten writing

The Egyptians invented writing. They needed it to keep count of all their wealth! They invented the 'picture-writing' that we call hieroglyphics.

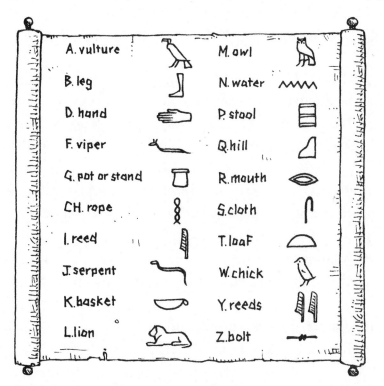

Now see if you can read this message – remember, the sound of the letters is more important than the English spelling.

43

Suffering soldiers

An Egyptian soldier's life was probably not as bad as student scribes tried to make out. The young writers wrote charming true-life notes like this one about soldiers:

> The common soldier has many, many officers all telling him what to do. The officers say things like, 'Get the men to work!' So the common soldier is woken after just an hour's sleep and worked until sunset. He is always hungry. He is like a dead man and yet he lives.

A bit like going to school today, isn't it?

Egypt had problems with invasions from bandits (who wanted to pinch their cattle), from tribes like 'The Sea People' who had lost their own land, and from other nations like the Hittites who wanted the power and wealth of Egypt.

The pharaohs needed armies to defend their land. But what do you know about them? Pick out the one *wrong* answer in each list below.

1 A soldier's weapons were...
   a stone-headed club, a spear, a bronze axe, a poison dart blower.

2 A common soldier protected himself with...
   a shield, a mop of thick hair, a helmet, a linen apron.

3 When soldiers weren't at war they had to work as....
   policemen, messengers, palace guards, firemen.

4 A soldier's chariot ha...
   tyres, weapon-racks, doors, two horses.

5 An Egyptian army travelled with...
   laundry women, weapon-makers, cooks, writers.

Answers:

1 A poison dart blower. The main weapon was the club (known today as a 'mace') to beat out your enemy's brains.

2 A helmet. Only the officers had helmets. The ordinary soldiers grew their hair thick to take the club blows and wore an apron to protect their naughty bits. Apart from that they didn't even wear shoes.

3 Firemen. The Egyptians had a good messenger service and soldiers took news from fortress to fortress so the pharaoh always knew what was happening. These forts were about 80 kilometres apart. They also used soldiers as a police force and of course to parade as the pharaoh's guards.

4 Doors. The Egyptians learned from Asia how to use horses but never rode them in battle – they only used them to pull chariots. Their chariots usually carried a driver and a warrior. The floor was made of woven leather because a solid floor would have given a bouncy, travel-sick-making ride. The wheels had leather tyres to hold them together. (They didn't have strong glue and screws in those days!)

5 Laundry women. As the soldiers only wore a loincloth, they didn't need anyone to do their washing for them. But they did take an army of cooks and weapon-makers and porters to carry their food and beer.

Quick Egyptian quiz

Why not pester a parent with this quick quiz and find out how much they know about the Awesome Egyptians?

1 The Egyptians made houses from bricks. The bricks were made from mud mixed with straw or something else. What? (Clue: not to be sniffed at)

2 Pilgrims came to ancient Egypt like holiday-makers to Blackpool. What miniature mummies did they buy as souvenirs? (Clue: did they have to kill these creatures nine times?)

3 A weaver who took a day off work would be punished. How? (Clue: you can't beat it)

4 Priests shaved off all their hair and eyebrows. Why? (Clue: not such a lousy idea)

5 Egyptian gods were often pictured with animal heads. Hapy had a baboon's head and Qebehsenuef had a falcon's. But Pharaoh Horemheb was buried with a rare god who had what sort of head? (Clue: flipping tortoise!)

6 The god Khnum created the first Egyptian people. What did the Egyptians believe he made them from? (Clue: they were earthy people)

7 Farmers scattered corn on their fields. How did they trample the seed in so the birds couldn't eat it all? (Clue: they were seen and herd)

8 Another way to keep birds off crops was to use scarecrows. These scarecrows were better than modern ones as they could run around screaming! How? (Clue: you must be kidding)

9 After reigning 30 years a pharaoh would have to prove his strength. How? (Clue: it was a good idea in the long run)

10 How many sides has an Egyptian pyramid? (Clue: slightly sneaky)

Answers:

1 Animal droppings. Poo! Imagine if your house was made of mud mixed with animal droppings! (Maybe it is!) And imagine mixing it in the days before rubber gloves had been invented. The Egyptians also burned animal droppings to make a fire.

2 Mummified cats. The cats had their necks broken, then were wrapped like a pharaoh's mummy. Pilgrims offered the cats to the gods. Vast cemeteries have been discovered with many thousands of these cat burials. It is likely that the animals were specially bred for this purpose. By 1900 hundreds of *tonnes* of mummified cats had been shipped to Liverpool to be ground up and used as fertilizer.

Horrible Histories note: Some school books tell you the Egyptians turned their cats to mummies because they loved their cute little kitties so much! Nice idea – load of rubbish.

3 He was beaten. Miss a day's work, weaver, and you get fifty lashes. And weaving was a tough job – you worked all day with your knees drawn up to your chest.

4 To keep free of lice. Everyone from pharaoh to peasant suffered from lice in the hair. Priests became slapheads to keep clean.

5 A turtle. It was not a common statue in Egypt so Horemheb probably had to shell out a lot of money to buy it!

6 Mud. The early Egyptians called themselves 'black-landers' because they believed they were made from the dark, rich soil by the River Nile. Khnum, they said, breathed life into them and the mud became human beings. Muddy marvellous!

7 With a herd of sheep, goats or pigs. These herds ran around the field and trampled in the grain. Don't try this at home.

8 They used children as scarecrows. Nowadays we'd probably use traffic wardens because they are scarier than anything.

9 He had to run around his palace. Some historians believe that in the early days of Egypt, if the king failed the test he would be sacrificed. He was literally running for his life!

10 Two. An in-side and an out-side. (Oh, come on! This is a *Horrible Histories* book! What did you expect? A *fair* question?)

THE GROOVY
GREEKS

By 356 BC the awesome Egyptians had had a pretty good run of 3,000 years as main Mediterranean men. But then along came the groovy Greeks. Mummies were now history and pyramids a thing of the past. So where exactly did these Greeks come from?

The ancient Greeks started building cities around 800 BC but each city had its own ruler. The strongest city-states were Athens and Sparta. They could have stayed separate, but the powerful Persians invaded in 490 BC so the Greeks joined together to beat them. Served the Persians right! Of course, Sparta and Athens fell out again.

Then 20-year-old Alexander the Great took over in 336 BC and set off to conquer the world – he pounded the problem Persians first, then he flattened the pharaohs and took over in Egypt.

How much do you know about gruesome Greek habits though?

Greek parties

The Greeks were great at throwing parties. But to be a good Greek guest you had to obey certain rules and do the right things at the right times! Just like today really, when you can throw confetti at a wedding … but would probably be locked away if you tried that trick at a funeral!

So here are some ancient Greek customs for weddings and funerals. Find out if you're a good guest by matching the right customs to the right events and answer: a wedding, a funeral or both.

Note: 'The main person' in the questions below is the bride or the groom if it's a wedding … the corpse if it's a funeral!

1 YOU SHOULD SACRIFICE A LUMP OF YOUR HAIR TO THE GODS BEFORE…
2 YOU SHOULD SHUT THE EYES AND THE MOUTH OF THE MAIN PERSON AT…
3 YOU SHOULD HAVE A TORCH-LIT PROCESSION AT…
4 YOU SHOULD BEAT YOUR HEAD AND TEAR YOUR HAIR AT…
5 YOU SHOULD GIVE THE MAIN PERSON A BATH BEFORE…
6 YOU SHOULD SING AND DANCE AT…
7 YOU SHOULD PLACE A CROWN ON THE HEAD OF THE MAIN PERSON AT…
8 YOU SHOULD THROW FRUIT AND NUTS…
9 YOU SHOULD GIVE GIFTS OF POTTERY, STONE VASES AND MIRRORS AT…
10 YOU SHOULD LEAVE THE PARTY EARLY IF YOU ARE A WOMAN AT…

Answers:
1 Both. You have to give the gods something so the happy couple (or the corpse) will be happy ever after. A bit of yourself would be best – but you don't want to go chopping off an ear! So hair is the next best thing.
2 A funeral. If you want your dead friend's spirit to leave the body peacefully you have to close their eyes and their mouth. Nice job for someone.

3 Both. Torches scare away evil spirits. Weddings take place at night and funerals in the early morning, so torches are also useful for making sure no one trips on a pothole and drops the corpse!

4 A funeral. The women get this cheerful job when they visit the corpse to say hello – or goodbye. The men simply raise their right hands as a salute to the gods. Don't Greek blokes have it easy?

5 Both. Brides, grooms and corpses have to go to their celebration clean, so they have to be bathed. A dead body can't do this for itself, of corpse. Another nice job for the women.

6 Both. The women (again) sing over the corpse at a funeral while the wedding procession sings as they tramp from the bride's father's house to the groom's house. They reckon it scares off evil spirits. (Bet you know some people who sing that badly!)

7 Both. It's your last look at your mouldering mate, so make them look their best with a crown. Also, they have to be dressed in an ankle-length robe. Very smart way to meet the gods. Both the bride and groom are crowned at a wedding feast.

8 A wedding. The bride eats an apple – to show all her food will now come from her husband. Then the guests shower the happy couple with fruit and nuts – which can hurt a lot more than confetti. (Just as well the Greeks didn't have coconuts to chuck!)

9 Both. The corpse is buried with some useful presents. The bride is given presents the morning after the wedding. The women guests have a procession to the house of the bride and groom while the men are probably having a lie-in after the wedding party last night!

10 A funeral. Women and men go separately to funerals. The women leave early to prepare the nosh and booze at the party afterwards. Work, work, work, girls. Eat, eat, eat, fellers!

As you can see weddings and funerals were similar in many ways. In both cases the Greeks believed you were sending someone off to a new life so they celebrated them in pretty much the same way.

As usual, women probably got the worst of the deal.

Woe for women

Being a female in ancient Greece wasn't much fun.

They were told what to do and what not to do – and didn't have anything like the freedom that the men enjoyed (those that weren't slaves, that is).

But could you sort out what to do and what not to do? Get it wrong and you may be punished! Which of the following statements are true and which are false?

1 A WOMAN MAY BUY OR SELL ANYTHING WORTH MORE THAN A SMALL MEASURE OF BARLEY.

2 A WOMAN MUST LEARN TO SPIN, WEAVE, COOK AND MANAGE SLAVES.

3 A WOMAN MUST WORSHIP THE GODDESS HESTIA.

4 A WOMAN MUST BE BROUGHT UP WITH SLAVES AND LEARN HOUSEHOLD SKILLS.

5 A WOMAN MUST STAY AT HOME.

6 A WOMAN MAY OWN THINGS OTHER THAN HER CLOTHES, JEWELLERY AND SLAVES.

7 A WOMAN OUGHT TO HAVE A HUSBAND (CHOSEN BY HER FATHER) WHEN SHE IS 15.

8 A WOMAN MUST NOT GO OUT EXCEPT TO VISIT OTHER WOMEN OR TO GO TO RELIGIOUS FESTIVALS, WEDDINGS AND FUNERALS.

9 A WOMAN MAY ALLOW ANYONE TO VISIT WITHOUT HER HUSBAND KNOWING.

10 A WOMAN MAY VOTE.

Answers:
1 false; 2 true; 3 true; 4 true; 5 true; 6 false; 7 true; 8 true; 9 false; 10 false.

Gruesome Greek quiz

Simply answer 'Yea' for yes or 'Nay' for no to these facts about the grisly Greeks.

1 In the story of Troy, King Agamemnon sacrifices his daughter to the gods. Would that have really happened in ancient Greece?

2 A slave called Aesop told great stories such as 'The Tortoise and the Hare'. He was richly rewarded by the Greek priests.

3 The people who lived in the city of Sparta were super-tough kids. One Spartan boy hid a stolen fox cub under his tunic and didn't let on, even though the fox ate the boy's guts away.

4 In Draco's Athens (c. 600 BC) the laws were strict and you could be whipped for stealing a cabbage.

5 Athens' ruler Peisistratus (605–527 BC) arranged to have himself attacked so the people would feel sorry for him.

6 Teacher Socrates taught his students not to believe in the old Greek gods. Socrates was hanged.

7 General Alcibiades (450–404 BC) wanted people to notice him. Once he cut off his dog's tail to get a bit of attention.

8 The Greeks read the future using the guts of dead birds.

9 Hecate was the Greek goddess of crossroads. Greeks left food at crossroads for her.

10 The Greeks painted the doors of their houses red with blood.

Answers:

1 Yea. At the time of the Trojan Wars, not only were children sacrificed but bits of them were eaten too. Aren't you glad you weren't around?

2 Nay. In fact they took him to the top of a cliff and threw him off. It seems a few of his stories upset them.

3 Yea. This was a popular story told by the Spartans. Of course it may have just been Spartan boasting and a big fib. But it's a warning – don't go sticking foxes (or bears or budgies) up your jumper!

4 Nay. Draco was *much* tougher than that! The punishment for pinching an apple or a cabbage was *death*! By the way, the punishment for idleness was also death! (Think of all those dead teachers in your school if we still had that law!)

5 Yea. Peisistratus staggered into Athens bruised and bleeding and said the city would suffer if its people didn't protect him. But he had arranged the attack on himself. The people of Athens were tricked into protecting him … even though they hated him.

6 Nay. He was sentenced to death by poisoning. And he had to drink the poison himself. Which he did. So he carried out his own death sentence. Why not ask your teacher to demonstrate how a brave teacher behaves?

7 Yea. Alcibiades was a pretty good Athenian general but switched sides to the Spartan enemies. But the Spartans didn't trust the traitor much. In the end he was murdered, shot full of Spartan arrows, and his dog would have wagged its tail in joy – if Alcibiades hadn't cut it off, that is.

8 Yea. Don't try this at home with your pet parrot. You'll make a right mess on the carpet. Stick to reading horoscopes in the newspaper.

9 Yea. She always had a pack of howling dogs with her. (If you want to carry on this ancient Greek habit then why not leave a tin of dog food at your nearest crossroads, eh? Seems a shame for Hecate to get all the grub.)

10 Nay. They painted them black with tar! They believed evil spirits would stick to the tar and be kept out. Messy.

Suffering Spartans

The Spartans were the toughest of all the Greek peoples – and it was extra-tough for Spartan kids.

Here's a Spartan rule book with some of the words missing. Get the answers right – or take a savage Spartan punishment!

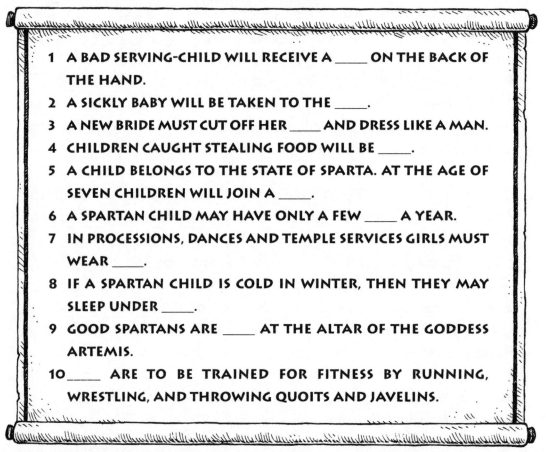

1 A BAD SERVING-CHILD WILL RECEIVE A _____ ON THE BACK OF THE HAND.

2 A SICKLY BABY WILL BE TAKEN TO THE _____.

3 A NEW BRIDE MUST CUT OFF HER _____ AND DRESS LIKE A MAN.

4 CHILDREN CAUGHT STEALING FOOD WILL BE _____.

5 A CHILD BELONGS TO THE STATE OF SPARTA. AT THE AGE OF SEVEN CHILDREN WILL JOIN A _____.

6 A SPARTAN CHILD MAY HAVE ONLY A FEW _____ A YEAR.

7 IN PROCESSIONS, DANCES AND TEMPLE SERVICES GIRLS MUST WEAR _____.

8 IF A SPARTAN CHILD IS COLD IN WINTER, THEN THEY MAY SLEEP UNDER _____.

9 GOOD SPARTANS ARE _____ AT THE ALTAR OF THE GODDESS ARTEMIS.

10 _____ ARE TO BE TRAINED FOR FITNESS BY RUNNING, WRESTLING, AND THROWING QUOITS AND JAVELINS.

The missing words, in the wrong order, are: no clothes, hair, herd, thistles, mountains, whipped, baths, girls, bite, beaten.

Answers:

1 Bite. Younger boys had to serve older boys. If the younger boy did something wrong he could be given a nasty nip!

2 Mountains. Babies were left up a mountain to die if they failed a health check.

3 Hair. And a bridegroom had to pretend to carry his bride off by force.

4 Beaten. Children were kept hungry and encouraged to steal food! (Spartans thought sneakiness was a handy skill in battle.) If the kids were caught stealing, they'd be beaten for being careless enough to get caught!

5 Herd. The toughest child was allowed to become leader and order the others about.

6 Baths. Stinky Spartans!

7 No clothes. So they didn't get fancy ideas about fine clothes.

8 Thistles. Children slept on beds of rushes that they gathered themselves from the river bank. In winter they could mix a few thistles in with the reeds – the prickles were supposed to give them a feeling of warmth!

9 Whipped. A horribly historical way to prove you were a good Spartan! The one who suffered the most lashes was the toughest. Some bled to death.

10 Girls. So don't mess with a Spartan miss.

Pythagoras says...

The potty Greek maths teacher Pythagoras had some strange beliefs. Why not play 'Pythagoras says' with your friends?

1 Sit in a circle on chairs.

2 You are Pythagoras and your friends are the pupils.

3 Shout an instruction from the list below.

4 If a player thinks Pythagoras really said it, then they have to jump to their feet and mime the action. If they are right, they get a point.

5 If they think Pythagoras never said it, they should stay seated. Anyone who sits when they should stand or stands when they should sit loses a point.

(NOTE: Pythagoras was a groovy Greek mathematician and *he* would've understood the rules even if your thick friends don't. Just get on with it and stop whingeing!)

Statements:

1 Pythagoras says don't help anyone to unload a cart!

2 Pythagoras says don't touch a white cockerel!

3 Pythagoras says don't slap a bald lion on the head!

4 Pythagoras says don't stand on your fingernail clippings!

5 Pythagoras says don't walk along a main street!

6 Pythagoras says don't touch the fire with an iron poker!

7 Pythagoras says don't go to sleep on a day that ends in a 'y'!

8 Pythagoras says don't eat beans!

9 Pythagoras says don't look in a mirror beside a lamp!

10 Pythagoras says don't pick your nose with your left hand!

Answers:

Pythagoras DID say 1, 2, 4, 5, 6, 8 and 9. And players should jump to their feet.

Pythagoras did NOT say 3, 7 and 10. And players should stay on their seats.

By the way, some Greeks like Pythagoras believed beans were the homes of dead people's spirits. That's why you shouldn't eat them. That tin in your kitchen may not be just baked beans – it could be human beans!

Terrible teacher

Alexander the Great was just a young man of 21 when he became ruler of the Greek Empire in 334 BC. Then he rampaged off to Persia, Egypt and as far as India gathering other empires.

How did he do that? Who taught him to conquer new nations?

Well, it wasn't Alex's dad, Macedonian King Philip. The king died … and some people think Alexander may have poisoned him!

No, Alex's teacher was the famous Greek scientist, Aristotle. Now old Aristotle had some potty ideas – he said that the gods made men to rule the world; women and slaves could not even think because they had such weak brains. Women and slaves were just there to do as men told them!

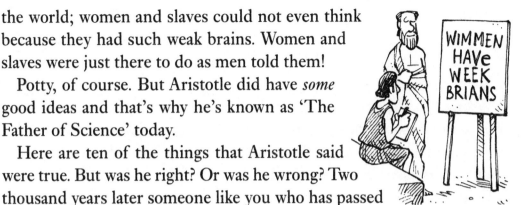

Potty, of course. But Aristotle did have *some* good ideas and that's why he's known as 'The Father of Science' today.

Here are ten of the things that Aristotle said were true. But was he right? Or was he wrong? Two thousand years later someone like you who has passed a Science SATs test should know. Let's find out! Simply answer 'right' or 'wrong' to Ari's ideas below...

1 The Earth is a sphere.

2 Thoughts come from the heart while the brain cools the blood.

3 Maggots grow from meat if it is left for too long.

4 The Sun, Moon and stars go around the Earth.

5 The Earth is *not* made up of tiny particles called atoms.

6 Earthquakes are caused by air trying to escape from the Earth.

7 The Greeks are the cleverest people on Earth.

8 Men are greater thinkers than women.

9 Drop a heavy object and drop a light object that are the same shape. The heavy object will fall faster.

10 Scientists should collect as many facts as possible.

Answers:

1 Right. Well done Ari! He knew that during an eclipse of the moon the shadow was curved ... so the Earth must be curved.

2 Wrong. Aristotle carved up more than 50 types of animals, insects, birds and fish to find out how they worked. But he couldn't ask them where their thoughts came from! Sorry, Ari.

3 Wrong. Maggots don't come from the meat itself. Maggots come from eggs laid on the meat by flies. The eggs hatch to become maggots and the maggots grow to be flies. Old Aristotle did not have a microscope to see the tiny fly eggs. You can get one from school – if looking at maggots hatching is your idea of fun!

4 Wrong. Aristotle was cleverer than some Greeks who said the Earth was flat! Yet there were other Greeks in Aristotle's day who believed that the Earth went around the Sun – which is right, as you'll know if you ever take a trip to the Sun!

5 Wrong. The Greek Democritus had said the Earth was made up of atoms. But Aristotle poked fun at him and said the Earth was made up of water, air, earth or fire or some mixture of those things. He said that the stars floated in a fifth element – ether. Wrong again, Ari.

6 Wrong. Aristotle believed that earth, air, fire and water tried to find their own levels – and air always tried to rise to the top. If air were trapped under the surface of the Earth then it would force its way out as a volcano, Aristotle believed. But *you* know it is liquid rock (magma) that forces its way up through the Earth's crust.

7 Wrong. Like Ari, some people still believe that one 'race' of people is better than another. That sort of thinking – racism – has led to a lot of hatred and a lot of misery.

8 Wrong. Sorry, lads, but it's just not true. Ancient Greek women were not taught to read or write because of Ari's potty idea. Those women could have made better scientists than him! (They couldn't have done much worse!)

9 Wrong. Try it. The scientist Galileo tested the idea by dropping objects off the famous Tower of Pisa. But you don't have to go to Pisa – Mount Everest would do.

10 Right. That is why Aristotle is the Father of Science. He made a lot of boobs, but he showed the rest of the human race how to study science. 'Gather the facts then make up your mind!' A bit like studying history really.

Alexander left Aristotle and went off to conquer the world, and Ari went back to Athens to teach. But Alex never forgot his old teacher and sent Ari animals from the countries he conquered – probably for teacher to chop up!

Horrible Hippocrates

Hippocrates (460–357 BC) was a Greek doctor who believed in the proper study of the body using experiments.

Hippocrates was so great that today's doctors still take the Oath of Hippocrates (though it has been altered in modern times) and promise:

I will give no deadly medicine to anyone if asked ... I will use treatment to help the sick but never to injure.

Hippo took samples from his patients and tested them. But he couldn't test them in a laboratory with chemicals the way modern doctors can. He

tested them by tasting them or by making his patient taste them.

But which of the following horrible things were tasted to test? Answer 'Yummy yes' or 'Nasty no'...

1 toenails	6 tears
2 vomit	7 skin
3 hair	8 snot
4 ear wax	9 spit
5 pus from infected wounds	10 pee

Answers:
1 Nasty no; 2 Yummy yes; 3 Nasty no; 4 Yummy yes; 5 Yummy yes; 6 Yummy yes; 7 Nasty no; 8 Yummy yes; 9 Nasty no; 10 Yummy yes.

Next time you feel poorly why not take a bottle of pee and snot along to your doctor and ask him to taste it?

Odd one out Olympics

There's a famous Greek poem written by Homer, *The Iliad,* that tells the story of the Greek attack on the city of Troy. The story is probably based on truth. Even today everyone knows the bit about the wooden horse of Troy – unless you're a wooden-headed toy.

But one of the forgotten bits is where Achilles organizes funeral games for his friend Patroclus who is killed during the Trojan war. The Greeks staged eight events on the plain outside Troy city, and legend says that these games were the origin of the famous Olympic Games.

What do you know about the old Olympics? Which is the odd one out in these lists?

1 Prizes in those first games included:
   cauldrons, gold, oxen, medals, women.

2 At the top athletic festivals the only prizes given were wreaths of leaves. The leaves could be:
   parsley, carrot, olive, laurel, celery.

3 When the winners got home they got extra rewards which could include:
   a pension, free meals, money, fame, free haircuts.

4 The sport of 'pancration' was a mix of boxing and wrestling where you could:
   strangle, bite off fingers, kick, arm-twist, jump up and down on your opponent.

5 The sports included:
   standing long-jump, horse-drawn chariot race, mule racing, javelin-throwing, swimming.

6   As the Olympics grew in size they added new competitions, including: junior Olympics for kids, married women's Olympics, music Olympics, speaking Olympics, drama Olympics.

7   The Hera Games for girls saw them dressed in a tunic which covered: the left breast, the right breast, the belly button, the thighs, the back.

8   The Greeks had their own names for their contests, of course. These contests included:
pugme, keles, hoplitodromos, diaulos, gymnasion.

9   The spoilsport Romans came along and banned the Olympics in AD 394. The games were *not* held in these years:
AD 394, 1896, 1916, 1940, 1944.

10 Sometimes a winner cheated by paying the judges. If he was caught the winner could:
be whipped, be made to pay for a statue of Zeus, lose the title, be banned from future games.

Answers:

1 Medals. Try giving the others away at your next school sports day! Women for prizes? A great way to get rid of your grotty sister, lads!

2 Carrot. Parsley's a funny sort of wreath but that's what you got at Nemea. You got olive at Olympia, laurel at Delphi and celery at Isthmia.

3 Free haircuts. According to the Roman author Plutarch, an Olympic victor who was a citizen of Athens could expect to receive in the year 600 BC a cash award of 500 drachmas, a fortune. An Isthmian victor would receive 100 drachmas. Athenian Olympic victors received a free  meal in the City Hall every day for the rest of their lives, a kind of early pension plan. How about free school dinners for life for your sports-day winners?

4 Bite off fingers. Nor could you rip off your opponent's ear and spit in the hole (as an English soccer player once threatened to do).

5 Swimming. There were relay running races where they used a flaming torch as a baton – dangerous, as the men ran naked! The main events were 200-metre and 400-metre running races. Quoit-throwing  was popular – seeing who could get nearest the target. A bit like giant tiddlywinks really.

6 Married women's Olympics. But there was a separate festival in honour of Hera (the wife of the Greek god Zeus). This festival included foot races for unmarried girls. But for the main Olympics  married women were banned! One woman who dressed as a man and sneaked in was caught. Her punishment was to be thrown off a high cliff ... where she did 100 metres faster than the runners. – 100 metres in a downward direction. Splat!

7 The right breast. The writer Pausanias gives us a description of a girl's costume for the Hera games of the 2nd century AD. The girls wore their hair free down their back and a tunic hanging almost as low as the knees covering only the left shoulder and breast.

8 Gymnasion. They did have: a pugme – a boxing event; a keles – a horse race; a hoplitodromos – a race in armour; and a diaulos – a foot race equal to two lengths of the stadium. But a gymnasion was where they trained – in Greek it meant 'a place of naked people'.

9 1896. The games *were* held in 1896 when Pierre de Coubertin, a French lord, revived them for the first time since AD 394. They were held every 4 years after 1896 but *not* during the First and Second World Wars.

10 Lose the title. They would usually be forced to pay for a new statue of the god Zeus, but the cheat would still be the winner. Who says 'Cheats never beats'?

Daft deaths

Not all Olympic champs died heroes. Some champs were chumps! Have a look at this unlucky lot and decide how they died. Award yourself a gold medal if you get all of these questions right!

1 Champion wrestler, Timanthese, lost his strength. He was so upset he did what?

a) He built a tower and threw himself off the top.

b) He built a fire and threw himself into it.

c) He built a pond and drowned himself in it.

2 Handsome Creugas and big bully Damoxenos fought to a standstill in a boxing match. The referee said they could each have one free shot at the other. Damoxenos killed Creugas with a cheat. What did he do?

a) He pulled a knife out of his hair band and stabbed Creugas.

b) He borrowed a nearby javelin and speared Creugas.

c) He used his sharp fingernails to rip Creugas's belly open and then pulled out his guts.

3 Wrestler Milo won five Olympic games as a wrestler and was super-strong. (He once held up the collapsing roof of a building while people escaped.) But he died when he tried his strength against what?

a) a lion

b) a tree

c) a woman

4 Wrestler Polydamas was another super-strong man. He once held a fierce bull so firmly it had to tear its own hoof off to escape. (Yeuch!) How did his strength finish him off?

a) He tried to copy Milo by holding up a collapsing roof.

b) He tried to copy Greek god Heracles by fighting a lion with his bare hands.

c) He tried to copy his old trick of ripping off a bull's hoof.

5 The Olympics were supposed to have started when King Oeomaus said to young Pelops, 'You want to marry my daughter? Then race me in a chariot.' Pelops won when King Oeomaus died. How?

a) Pelops nobbled Oeomaus's chariot.

b) Pelops nobbled Oeomaus's horses.

c) Pelops nobbled Oeomaus's drink.

Answers:

1b) Now that's what you call a bad loser!

2c) Damoxenos killed Creugas ... but lost the competition. The referee said the fighters could have one free shot at the enemy. When Damoxenos jabbed Creugas's stomach open with his hand, that was his one shot ... but ripping out his guts was a second movement. So dead Creugas was named the winner! (But he didn't get to go up and collect the prize.)

3b) The tree was split and he jammed his hands in the split to rip it apart. But it sprang back and trapped his hands. Wild animals came along and made a meal of miserable Milo's mighty muscles.

NIBBLE NIBBLE NIBBLE

4a) He *did* copy Heracles and kill a lion bare-hande, but he survived that. Then, one summer, Polydamas and his friends were relaxing in a cave when the roof began to crumble down upon them. Thinking his huge strength could stop the cave-in, Polydamas held his hands up to the roof, trying to keep it in place as the rocks crashed down around him. His friends ran from the cave and reached safety, but the wrestler died there. Final result: Cave 1, Polydamas 0.

5a) Pelops paid Oeomaus's servant to damage the king's chariot axle. The axle broke and king Oeomaus was dragged to his death by his horses. Pelops got the princess and got the throne. But don't feel too sorry for Oeomaus. He had beaten 13 other young men – and had their heads cut off! Bad losers are one thing, but Oeomaus was a rotten winner!

Quick Greek quiz

Everyone studies the Greeks at school. Greek history lessons were even around when your teachers went to school, so they should know the answers to these ten quick questions.

1 General Alcibiades hated the Greek gods and damaged their statues. He smashed off what part of the statues? (Clue: he only did this to the male gods)

2 The superstitious Greeks did not like dreaming of seeing your own face in a mirror. What did they think you would do soon after? (Clue: never see your face in a mirror again!)

3 Around 375 BC the girls of Attica went to the local temple and ran round the woods pretending to be bears. What did they wear? (Clue: don't try this at the North Pole)

4 Greek teacher Aristotle had a favourite food that you will probably never eat. What? (Clue: unless you are stranded in the Sahara desert)

5 Playwright Aeschylus died (it is said) when an eagle dropped an animal on his head. What? (Clue: a slow death?)

6 Greek teacher Gorgias was born in a strange place. In his mother's what? (Clue: he was dead lucky to be alive, but Mum wasn't.)

7 Greeks invented a nasty weapon. It was a liquid that caught fire as soon as it landed and set fire to everything it touched in open air. What was it called? (Clue: not Roman water but…)

8 Aesculapius was a Greek doctor. Some of his cures worked. Some of the stories of other cures are plain daft. How did he cure (they say) water on a girl's brain? (Clue: she got it in the neck)

9 Doctor Hippocrates practised cutting out a circle of the skull to drain fluids off the brain. But why did the patient take home the circle of bone? (Clue: like a rabbit's foot?)

10 Some vegetarian Greeks refused to sacrifice animals to the gods. What did they sacrifice instead? (Clue: obvious really!)

Answers:

1 Their naughty bits. Alcibiades knocked off the naughty bits on the statues of the naked gods. Ouch!

2 Die. Mind you, some people are so hideous they'd probably die if they saw themselves in a mirror awake! (Bet you know people like that!)

3 Nothing. This was supposed to prepare them for being grown women. The crazy chases were supposed to get the last wild bits of fun out of them before they became boring adults.

4 Camel. Maybe we should start serving camel at posh tea parties. You turn to your guest and say, 'One hump or two?'

5 A tortoise. We do *not* know how the tortoise was after the accident. If it lived it was probably a bit shell-shocked though.

6 Coffin. Georgias's mother died and was popped in a coffin but somehow the baby was born anyway. He grew up and taught his students, 'Nothing exists – not even me!' If I'd been his student I'd have just skived off school then!

7 Greek Fire. Even today no one is sure how Greek Fire was made. But it was nasty stuff. Not the sort of thing you'd want to spray on your barbecue.

8 He cut off her head. After the water drained off he sewed the head back on. Hummmm! Believe that and you are ready for a new head yourself!

9 For luck. The superstitious Greeks kept the bone as a good-luck charm. It was supposed to keep you safe from disease.

10 Vegetables. They killed carrots, cracked corn and carved cabbages cruelly and then they probably battered some poor beans brutally. Vile vegetarians, how could they?

THE ROTTEN ROMANS

Even the groovy Greeks gave way in the end. Along came a more powerful people – the rotten Romans. They grew from a group of villages in Italy filled with criminals and slaves. At first they had kings – but they were thrown off their thrones for being too wicked in 509 BC.

For the next 500 years the Romans were ruled by their most powerful lords who picked a couple of leaders called consuls. By 146 BC the rotten Romans, with their cool consuls, had conquered the Greeks. The last consul with real power, mighty Julius Caesar, was murdered and in 27 BC his adopted son became the first Roman emperor, Augustus. Now the ruthless Romans were really ready to rule the world.

The Romans probably had the world's largest empire – until the Brits came along and took over a quarter of the world in Queen Victoria's time (the 1800s). How did the Romans rampage round the world so well? By being really rotten, of course. They had some of the wiliest warriors, horriblest habits and some of the looniest leaders in the whole of horrible history. How much do you know about them?

Evil emperors

It's really weird but true. Some of the battiest people in history have been leaders – kings and queens, emperors and empresses, presidents and princes. It's almost as if you *have to be* slightly potty to be a ruler!

Rome had their fair share of rotten rulers. Here are a few foul facts about them. Only the odd word has been left out for you to complete...

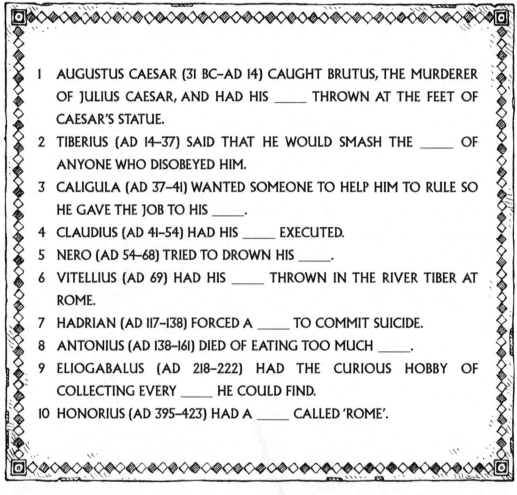

1 AUGUSTUS CAESAR (31 BC–AD 14) CAUGHT BRUTUS, THE MURDERER OF JULIUS CAESAR, AND HAD HIS _____ THROWN AT THE FEET OF CAESAR'S STATUE.

2 TIBERIUS (AD 14–37) SAID THAT HE WOULD SMASH THE _____ OF ANYONE WHO DISOBEYED HIM.

3 CALIGULA (AD 37–41) WANTED SOMEONE TO HELP HIM TO RULE SO HE GAVE THE JOB TO HIS _____.

4 CLAUDIUS (AD 41–54) HAD HIS _____ EXECUTED.

5 NERO (AD 54–68) TRIED TO DROWN HIS _____.

6 VITELLIUS (AD 69) HAD HIS _____ THROWN IN THE RIVER TIBER AT ROME.

7 HADRIAN (AD 117–138) FORCED A _____ TO COMMIT SUICIDE.

8 ANTONIUS (AD 138–161) DIED OF EATING TOO MUCH _____.

9 ELIOGABALUS (AD 218–222) HAD THE CURIOUS HOBBY OF COLLECTING EVERY _____ HE COULD FIND.

10 HONORIUS (AD 395–423) HAD A _____ CALLED 'ROME'.

Missing words, in the wrong order: mother, head, chicken, horse, corpse, cobweb, cheese, wife, wrinkly, leg.

Answers:

1 Head. Nice present for Jules!

2 Leg. Tiberius died at the age of 78, probably suffocated by his chief helper.

3 Horse. Cruel Caligula liked to feed criminals to wild animals. He was stabbed to death by one of his guards.

4 Wife. She was a bit of a flirt. But he also had 300 of her party friends chopped too! His third wife, and niece, had him poisoned with mushrooms.

5 Mother. When the plot failed he sent soldiers to give her the chop. Nero stabbed himself to death before his enemies got to him.

6 Corpse. He was murdered in the centre of Rome but not given a nice emperor's burial.

7 Wrinkly. Hadrian accused Servianus of treason and forced him to kill himself. But Servianus was 90 years old and hardly a big threat.

8 Cheese. At least that's what a Roman historian blamed his death on. Guess it was just hard cheese.

9 Cobweb. Maybe he was planning to build the world's first web-site?

10 Chicken. Trouble is he loved the chicken Rome more than he loved the city Rome, and the city was neglected.

Stabbing Jules

Julius Caesar was a brilliant Roman leader, but he became a bit too big for his boots – his red boots, in fact. The Romans were now used to having leaders who were 'elected'. They had hated their old kings ... who had worn red boots instead of a crown, but when the booted-up kings were kicked out the Romans got on much better with their elected leaders.

But Julius got himself elected for life. Just like a king. When he started wearing red boots, his number was up. There was just one way to get rid of him then – assassination.

His friend Brutus led the murderers, who struck when Caesar was entering the Roman parliament (the senate). Roman writer Plutarch told the gory story. Can you sort out the scrambled words in this version?

> Some of Brutus's gang slipped behind Caesar's chair while others came to meet him. Cimber grabbed Caesar's robe and pulled it from his neck. This was the A SLING for the attack.
>
> Casca struck the first blow. His IF KEN made a wound in ASS ACRE neck but Caesar was able to turn round, grab the knife and hold on. The HAT CREWS were horrified but didn't dare move or make a sound.
>
> Each AS SINS AS bared his dagger now. They pushed Caesar this way and that like a wild BE SAT surrounded by hunters.
>
> Brutus stabbed Caesar in the groin. Above all Caesar had RED TUTS Brutus. When he saw Brutus coming towards him he pulled his robe over his head and sank down.
>
> The attackers pushed Caesar against the ASTUTE of his old enemy Pompey. The statue became drenched with DO LOB.
>
> Caesar received 23 wounds. Many of the assassins WON DUDE each other as they fought to stick so many knives into one body.

Answers:
These are the unscrabbled words in the correct order: signal; knife; Caesar's; watchers; assassin; beast; trusted; statue; blood; wounded.

Twenty-three wounds! He must have ended up looking like a porcupine – a very dead, very red porcupine. But Jules's mate, Mark Antony, took revenge on the assassins and the Romans went on to have many far worse emperors.

70

Funny 'n' foul emperor facts

Can you work out which of these weird emperor facts are true and which are false?

1 You could be executed for saying the word 'goat' near Caligula.

2 Claudius usually had a runny nose.

3 A doctor saved Claudius from poisoning by making him vomit with a feather.

4 Nero played the fiddle and watched while Rome burned.

5 Otho (AD 69) used wet bread as after-shave.

6 Commodus (AD 180–192) enjoyed shooting the heads off ostriches with his bow and arrow.

7 In AD 217 Empress Julia Domna stuffed herself with so much food that she burst.

8 Eliogabalus made his ministers carry sheep guts to the temple as a gift for the gods.

9 Gordian (AD 238) hanged himself with his shoelaces.

10 Victorinus (AD 269–271) was killed for chatting up a soldier's wife.

Answers:

1 True. He was very hairy all over his body – like a goat. So he was very touchy and anyone saying the 'g' word would be executed. *But* he didn't have much of that hair on his head. So he hated it if anyone looked down on his bald spot. Looking *down* on Caligula got you executed too!

2 True. He was a bit of a mess all round. His head shook, his knees wobbled, his mouth foamed and his voice stammered.

3 False. The doctor was part of the plot to poison him. When the first lot of poison failed to kill Claudius the doctor offered to make him vomit by tickling his throat with a feather. But the feather was soaked in even *more* poison and finished Claudius off!

71

4 False. This is a popular story but it just isn't true. Nero wasn't in Rome when the fire started. When he heard about it he hurried back and organized the fire-fighting. Of course fiddles hadn't been invented, but Nero *did* play the lyre (probably very badly).

5 True. Don't ask me why, though. Emperors always seem to have had too much dough! His hair was so thin he wore a wig and had every hair of his body plucked out. Ouch!

6 True. He used wide-headed arrows. As the ostriches ran round in circles he sliced off their heads. The birds kept running round … like headless chickens!

7 False. She starved herself to death because she was afraid Emperor Macrinus would torture her.

8 True. He made important people, not the servants, carry the sheep and cattle guts as part of the daily sacrifices.

9 False. He hanged himself with his belt when he heard his son had been killed fighting for him. Gordian ruled for just 22 days.

10 True. He made a habit of it. The husbands got jealous. One got very jealous indeed and had a victorious fight with Victorinus.

Awful army

The Romans were famous for their army. They were well organized and well armed. They were also mainly foreigners. The conquered peoples around the empire joined the Roman army and conquered other peoples who joined the Roman army and conquered … and so on until they ran out of conkers.

But how much of the terrible truth do you know about these super soldiers?

1 If you were a beaten tribesman but refused to fight in the Roman army what could happen to you?
a) You would be forced to do all the washing up for the Roman army.
b) You would have your hair cut off so everyone could see you were a coward.
c) You would have your head cut off so everyone could see what happened to trouble-makers.

2 What did the Roman soldier wear under his leather kilt?
a) nothing
b) a fig leaf
c) underpants

3 Who paid for a soldier's food, uniform, weapons ... and burial?
a) The emperor paid for everything.
b) The general paid for his soldiers out of his wages.
c) The soldier paid for himself out of his wages.

4 If you joined the Roman army how long did you have to stay in it?
a) 3 years
b) 25 years
c) 40 years

5 What would you use instead of toilet paper in the army toilets?
a) your underpants
b) a sponge on a stick
c) your sword

6 Who could a Roman soldier marry?
a) no one
b) a slave
c) a Roman

7 How tall did you have to be to be a Roman soldier?
a) under 1.6 metres
b) between 1.6 and 1.8 metres
c) over 1.8 metres

8 One Roman centurion was known as 'Give me another'. Why?
a) He was a greedy turnip and ate one chicken after another, always crying, 'Give me another!'
b) He was a sad bloke crying 'Give me my mother!' but his deaf soldiers heard him wrongly.
c) He was a bully who cried, 'Give me another!' every time he smashed a stick over a soldier as he beat him.

9 Roman spear-heads snapped off when they hit something. Why?
a) They were made of rubbish British iron.
b) The Romans made them to break off.
c) They weren't real spears, they were just for show.

10 An army doctor would treat you and not hear your screams. Why not?
a) He was trained not to listen.
b) His eardrums were burst as part of his doctor training.
c) Doctors were forbidden to wash ear wax out of their ears.

Answers:

1c) You have to fight for Rome, which is a real pain in the neck. If you don't it's a *real* pain in the neck.

2c) Can you blame them? Go to Hadrian's Wall in winter and see how cold it gets. You'd want to wear five pairs of knickers!

3c) Paying for your own burial is a bit tough. If I were a dead Roman soldier I'd refuse to pay!

4b) Unless you were killed, of course, in which case you were in it for life!

5b) The sponge was dipped in water (cold), used, then rinsed and left for the next person. Hmmm! Try it next time you run out of a roll.

6a) At least, they weren't supposed to marry. But many soldiers had wives outside the camp.

7b) But this rule was often broken if the army was desperate for men. Of course, if you wanted to dodge the army you could cut off your head and you'd probably be too short! (*Horrible Histories* are full of cool ideas like that!)

8c) It was a hard life when your centurion could beat you for the slightest little thing. But no different from schools in the 1950s. (Ask your grandad!).

9b) The idea was that they hit their enemy. But if they missed and the head snapped off, then the enemy couldn't throw them back.

10a) You may well have a school dentist a bit like that.

Gory gladiators

A Roman writer said...

> *Gladiators were men who fought with swords in the amphitheatre and other places for the amusement of the Roman people*

Another Roman writer, Seneca, went to see the Roman 'games' and wrote...

> I HAPPENED TO DROP IN ON THE MIDDAY SPORT IN THE ARENA. I WAS LOOKING FOR A LITTLE (1) _____ BUT SAW ONLY (2) _____, PURE AND SIMPLE. THE FIGHTERS HAVE NOTHING TO PROTECT THEM. THEIR BODIES ARE OPEN TO EVERY BLOW, AND EVERY BLOW FINDS ITS MARK. THEY ARE LASHED FORWARD SO THEY CAN'T ESCAPE THE (3) _____.
>
> IN THE MORNING MEN FIGHT (4) _____ AND BEARS, AT NOON THEY FIGHT EACH OTHER. THE (5) _____ FIGHT AGAIN AND AGAIN UNTIL THEY ARE DEFEATED. (6) _____ IS THE FIGHTER'S ONLY WAY OUT. THE (7) _____ SAY, 'BUT THESE MEN ARE HIGHWAY (8) _____ AND (9) _____. THEY DESERVE ALL THEY ARE GETTING!' CAN'T YOU SEE HOW WRONG THIS (10) _____ IS?

Missing words, not in the correct order: butchery, lions, death, robbers, sport, entertainment, murderers, spectators, winners, swords.

Answers:
1 entertainment; 2 butchery; 3 swords; 4 lions; 5 winners; 6 death; 7 spectators; 8 robbers; 9 murderers; 10 sport.

Seneca was banned from Rome for eight years for daring to say that about Emperor Caligula's sport! (Don't feel too sorry for Seneca – he was not a nice man!)

Choose your gladiator

Gladiators weren't all exactly the same. There were all sorts of different types. Here are a few you might like to try copying… using a rolled-up newspaper as a weapon, of course.

But first, can you match the gladiator to his title? But beware! To make it extra tricky there are *two* fake names in there!

1 ANDABATAE – CLUE: NEED A GUIDE DOG
2 DIMACHERI – CLUE: AMBIDEXTROUS?
3 ORDINARII – CLUE: PLAIN AND SIMPLE
4 SPINACHERI – CLUE: TRAINED, LIKE POPEYE ON SPINACH
5 HOPLOMACHI – CLUE: GOOD KNIGHT?
6 LAQUEATORES – CLUE: NO NOOSE IS BAD NOOSE
7 RETIARII – CLUE: THEY HAD A POINT – OR MORE
8 BEEFABURGI – CLUE: KILLS BULLS FOR THE EMPERORS BURGERS
9 SECUTORES – CLUE: SHIELDED
10 BESTIARII – CLUE: BEASTLY

MOO!

Answers:

1j) These gladiators wore helmets with no eye slits – so they were fighting blindfold! Some modern historians have said andabatae fought on horseback but that's almost certainly not true.

2c) These clever gladiators fought with two swords. So they couldn't have held a shield, of course. Once they'd cut through their enemy's defences, they must have been a bit like a food processor and made them into mincemeat.

3d) Now this may surprise you but they were ordinary gladiators. That is, they fought one-to-one with other ordinary ordinarii. You still have that sort of fighting in school playgrounds. To think it's been going on for 2,000 years is quite extraordinarii.

4g) Sorry, they didn't exist.

5i) They fought in a complete suit of armour. Sounds like the right sort of gladiator job to get. Imagine facing a lion while you're wearing the armour. Once he'd snapped his teeth and claws on your metal skin you could kill it. Cheating a bit, is that.

6f) These cowboy gladiators used a noose to capture their opponents. This sounds quite loopy.

7b) These gladiators fought with just a three-pointed lance (or trident) and a net. This is very useful if you're going fishing but a bit dangerous if you are up against a man with a sword. Throw your net and stab him while he's tangled up – but if you miss you have to run away to give yourself time to gather your net for another throw.

8a) Sorry, no such thing.

9e) Gladiators armed with sword and shield, usually up against the retiarius with his net. If he missed with the net you chased him and tried to kill him.

10h) These were people who fought against wild animals. If you were lucky you went to a beast-fighting school and learned how to kill them. You were given weapons and were expected to win and live.

Of course, not many of the gladiators wanted to go in to the arena and fight to the death … and who can blame them? So they were forced in by attendants carrying whips and red-hot irons.

If you were a criminal you were really unlucky – you'd be sent in unarmed. The beasts were expected to kill you, tear you apart and eat you. Don't try this at home with your pet poodle as you will make a terrible mess on the carpet and your parents will have to pay a fortune to have it cleaned.

Foul Roman food

Romans loved food. The rich could afford all sorts – the poor, as usual in history, ate whatever they could get their choppers round.

Do you know what the rotten Romans ate? Have a go at this quirky quiz on cuisine (that's a posh word for 'cooking') and find out...

1 The Romans didn't have tomato ketchup but they did have sauce made from what?
a) sheep eyeballs
b) fish guts
c) elephant's tail

2 At posh Roman feasts guests ate more than their stomachs could hold. How?
a) They emptied their stomachs by vomiting every now and then.
b) They stretched their stomachs with special exercises.
c) They stuck a pin in their stomach to let out trapped air and let in more food.

3 Snails were fattened up before they were killed. They were kept in a bowl of what?
a) chopped cabbage
b) brains
c) blood

4 Emperor Eliogabalus served 600 of them at one feast. What?
a) ostrich brains
b) ducks' feet
c) camel-burgers

5 Emperor Eliogabalus also served a meal where the peas were mixed with what?
a) queues
b) poison
c) gold nuggets

6 A Roman called Trimalchio had a feast with a roasted boar. When it was sliced down the belly, what came out?
a) maggots
b) songbirds
c) a dancing girl

7 What could you watch as you ate at some Roman feasts?
a) television
b) two gladiators trying to murder one another
c) tap-dancing bears

8 The Romans ate cute little pets that you probably wouldn't eat. What?
a) cats
b) budgies
c) dormice

9 The Romans did *not* eat animals' what?
a) teeth
b) brains
c) lungs

10 Emperor Maximian was a strange eater. Why?
a) He was the only vegetarian emperor.
b) He ate only eggs and drank only water.
c) He ate 20 kilos of meat a day.

Answers:
1b) The guts were soaked in salt water and left to stew in the sun for a few days. Then the fish-gut sauce was poured over the food as a tasty treat. Oh my cod!
2a) They went to a special room called a vomitorium and threw up. They used a stick with a feather to tickle their tonsils and vomited into a bowl. When their stomach was empty they went back and ate more. Scoff-vomit, scoff-vomit, scoff-vomit all night long. Good idea for school dinners?
3c) The snails supped the blood till they were too fat to get in their shells. The blood diet made them taste nice. If they wanted creamy snails, the Romans fed them on milk before eating them.

4a) Ostrich brains are quite small so he'd need 600 to keep his guests fed. But where did he get all those ostriches? Zoo knows?

5c) Eliogabalus mixed gold and precious stones with the peas as a sort of treat. But if one of those diamonds smashed your teeth you'd be sore. And if you swallowed a gold nugget you'd be ill! You'd have to sit on the toilet and wait for some change!

6b) There were thrushes stuffed inside the roast boar. (Were they bored in there?) Trimalchio also served wine that was 100 years old at that feast.

7b) Of course, the trouble with gladiators fighting as you eat is that they could splash blood and guts all over your freshly cooked dinner. Aren't you lucky you don't suffer that while you watch telly?

8c) They fed the dormice really well on walnuts, acorns and chestnuts. They were served roasted and stuffed with pork sausage. Scrummy! Even tastier than hamster or gerbil!

9a) They ate all sorts of other things though. As well as sheep and goat lungs or brains, they ate gulls, peacocks, swans and jackdaws. They stuffed the birds just by pushing stuffing straight down their throats. They didn't clean the insides out the way you do with your Christmas turkey. Yeuch!

10c) That's about a small sheep every day. Would ewe believe it? He was also supposed to have drunk about 34 litres of wine … but it must have been very weak. Of course, after 20 years all that eating killed him, but he was probably too drunk to notice he was dead!

Funny funerals

Here are ten questions about rotten Roman funerals. Can you guess which of the answers is correct?

1 A Roman law said women at funerals must not…
a) eat sweets as they walked down the street behind the coffin
b) tear at their cheeks with their fingernails to show how unhappy they were

2 To save themselves suffering the awful smell of a dead body the mourners…
a) wore clothes pegs on their noses
b) covered the corpse in sweet spices and perfumes

3 The writer Ovid said funerals were…
a) good places to chat up girls
b) bad places for catching colds

4 At the funeral of Julius Caesar the people watched…
a) a mechanical dummy revolving to show the 23 stab wounds
b) a fly-past of 23 trained pigeons

I'VE BEEN POOPED-ON BY A PROCESSION PIGEON

5 Caesar's funeral was unusual because it was…
a) held twice when a rainstorm put out the funeral fire at the first try
b) held in the city and not in the countryside even though that was against the law

6 Bodies were carried to funerals…
a) standing up
b) lying down

7 A Roman boy died and was cremated, and then his mother had a funeral because…
a) she heard about the death too late and missed the cremation
b) she enjoyed the first one so much she wanted to do it all over again

8 Not all Romans were cremated or buried, some were turned into mummies by…
a) soaking the body in honey
b) stuffing the body with cotton-wool

9 When the son of Roman Regulus died his father threw...
a) all of the boy's ponies, dogs and birds on to the funeral fire
b) himself on to the funeral fire

10 After a funeral the guests would sit by the graveside and...
a) have a laugh
b) have a meal

Answers:

1b); 2b); 3a); 4a); 5b); 6a); 7a); 8a); 9a); 10b).

Caesar's wax dummy also had an actor speaking in Caesar's voice and naming the murderers. Creepy, eh? People reported seeing him going up to heaven. Hope they had plenty of mops in heaven to soak up all that blood!

Quick Roman quiz

Why not pester your parents and find out how much they know about the rotten Romans with this quick quiz?

1 In AD 64 Rome had a great fire. Emperor Nero blamed the Christians. How did he punish them? (Clue: let the punishment fit the crime!)

2 Why were there no dead bodies in Rome? Well, not for more than a couple of days. (Clue: they weren't buried in the dead centre of Rome)

3 Roman kids used a bit of a pig for a ball. What bit did they use? (Clue: a load of tripe)

4 If a gladiator fell but wasn't quite dead then a servant finished him off. How? (Clue: that's hitting the nail on the head)

5 A poisonous Roman spider bites you. You crush its body into the wound to cure it. But what do you use if you can't catch the spider? (Clue: search the internet)

6 The Romans cut off Saint Alban's head for being a Christian. As Alban's head hit the ground the executioner clutched at his own eyes. Why? (Clue: that's what you do when pupils fall out)

7 What did rich Romans do if a tooth fell out? (Clue: not true)

8 A father was the ruler of the family. What was the harshest punishment he could give a wicked son? (Clue: the son would never be wicked again!)

9 In AD 71 Spartacus led a slave rebellion. It ended when 6,000 slaves were executed along the side of a road. How did they die? (Clue: they were very cross.)

10 Chariot races were between four teams – reds, greens, blues and whites. They often caused fights to break out. Who fought? (Clue: too easy to need a clue!)

Answers:

1 He burned them alive. Rome had seven fire brigades and they all failed to control the Great Fire. They also failed to put out the burning Christians. The firemen also acted as sort of night-watch policemen. With two jobs, up all night, they were probably too sleepy to notice the Great Fire!

2 They were all buried outside the city. Julius Caesar passed a law saying cremations and burials must take place outside the city. This was to keep diseases out of the city. Well, you wouldn't want a mouldy body in your back garden, would you?

3 The pig's stomach. They knotted it at each end, then blew it up. Would you fancy giving a kiss of life to a pig's belly? They played ball games like 'trigon' – rather like passing a balloon between three people.

4 With a hammer blow to the head. This was cleaner than a chop with a sword. After all, these servants had to keep sprinkling sand in the arenas to soak up the blood and stop fresh gladiators slipping. So a hammer-smack saved on sand!

5 The spider's web. And crushed frogs drunk in wine are a good cure for toad-poison. It's no worse than some things you eat in burger bars.

6 His eyes fell out. At least that's what the legend says. But it may just be true, so don't go around lopping off saintly heads – unless you want a real close-up view of your shoelaces.

7 Got a false tooth. Romans made false teeth out of gold or ivory. And they kept their teeth clean using tooth powder. One tooth powder was made of mouse-brains – to keep their teeth squeaky clean?

8 Execution. Usually they made do with a good whipping or maybe sold the boy as a slave. But don't tell your parents this rotten Roman trick. It might give them ideas!

9 They were crucified. No one is quite sure if Spartacus was crucified or died in battle. But it's a great story that has been turned into books and films and computer games and even a ballet. (No, it was a modern computer game, not a Roman computer game, dummy!)

10 The fans. Just like modern soccer matches the fans had their favourites and the real boneheads wanted to give rival fans a kicking. Not a lot has changed in 2,000 years, has it?

THE MAD MAYA

Of course you know that the first human towns and cities formed in the 'Middle East'. But thousands of years ago some people crossed into north America and spread down to south America. (North America and Asia were joined by a strip of land in those times.)

In Central America, the Mayan people were top dogs for a long while. They disappeared, like all the ancients, but a lot of their ideas lived on with the people who followed them. People like the Aztecs.

Of all the horrible people in *Horrible History* the Aztecs must have been about the horriblest! Their favourite way of dealing with enemies was to rip out their heart while it was still beating. So what do you know about the mad Maya and the awful Aztecs?

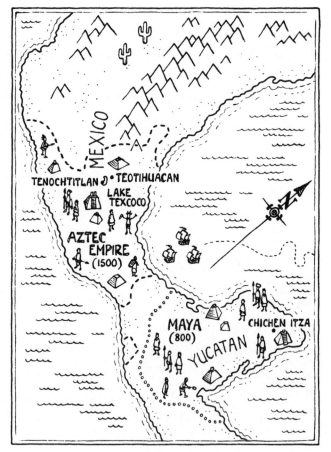

Murderous Maya

The Maya had some very strange customs and some rather nasty ones. Could you have lived like a Maya? Try this mix and match quiz…

1   HUNGRY MAYAN CHILDREN SNACKED BY...

2   THE MAYA MADE A GIFT TO THE GODS BY...

3   A MAYAN MOTHER WOULD SAVE HER NEWBORN BABY FROM EVIL BY...

4   YOUNG MAYAN CHILDREN WERE DECORATED BY...

5   MAYAN MOTHERS MADE THEIR CHILDREN 'BEAUTIFUL' BY...

6   THE MAYA USED GIRLS WHEN THEY WANTED TO SPEAK TO THE GODS BY...

7   THE MAYA CHEATED WHEN THEY WENT FISHING BY...

8   WHEN A MAYAN BABY DIED ITS MOTHER SHOWED SORROW BY...

9   NOBLE MAYAN BABIES WERE MADE TO LOOK LESS 'COMMON' BY...

10 A MAYAN MAN WHO STOLE ANOTHER MAN'S WIFE WAS EXECUTED BY...

A) STRAPPING BOARDS TO THE CHILDREN'S SKULLS TO GIVE THEM NARROW HEADS.

B) EATING MAGGOTS FROM A WASP'S NEST.

C) IGNORING THE BABY FOR THREE DAYS.

D) CUTTING OFF THE END OF ONE FINGER.

E) GIVING THEIR OWN BLOOD.

F) HAVING A ROCK DROPPED ON HIS HEAD.

G) THROWING THEM DOWN A WELL AT SUNRISE.

H) DANGLING ORNAMENTS THROUGH HOLES IN THEIR EARS, NOSE AND LIPS.

I) THROWING DRUGS IN THE RIVER.

J) MAKING THEM CROSS-EYED.

Answers:

1b) The muddy wasp nests were heated up until sweating wasp maggots wriggled out. Then the Maya would instantly grab them and dig into a nice warm snack. Yum!

2e) They would use spines from a stingray's tail to prick themselves and give blood. Mayan boys would give blood from the ears, the elbows and their naughty bits for important religious festivals! Girls had it easier and could instead pull a rope of thorns through a hole in their tongue!

3c) That way evil spirits wouldn't notice there was a new body around to attack. The mother would also tie ropes around the baby's wrists and ankles so its soul wouldn't escape.

4h) A bit like today's children!

5j) Doting mums fastened a ball of wax on to their baby's head-board (or to the hair on their forehead) and let it dangle in front of their noses until their eyes crossed.

6g) At noon the girls were fished out of the well and asked, 'What did the gods say to you?' Whatever they replied the Maya would believe.

7i) The Maya would use dams to block off streams and then throw drugs into the water. When the knocked-out fish floated to the surface they could be easily picked out of the river.

8d) The fingertip would be buried with the child.

9a) The Maya had broad heads, so the Mayan lords decided their children should have narrow heads so they didn't look common. Sometimes the heads were bound so that the skull would become egg-shaped with the point at the back.

10f) The angry husband was allowed to kill the wicked wife-stealer.

Mayan medicine

The Maya had some very strange cures. Would you like to try any of the following top ten tasty treats … even if you were dying? But which are true Mayan medicines and which are false?

1 Eating shredded cockerel feathers.
2 Smoking tobacco to cure snake bites!
3 Drinking camel's blood.
4 Eating bats' wings.
5 Drinking your own pee out of your shoe.
6 Swallowing powdered dolphin.
7 Eating dried tapir droppings.
8 Drinking a whole bat dissolved in honey wine.
9 Eating moose's brains.
10 Swallowing red worms.

Mathematical Maya

The Maya were clever at maths and astronomy and
developed their own incredible calendar that lots of
Central America nations copied for over a thousand
years. They also had a form of picture-writing and
a system of numbers:

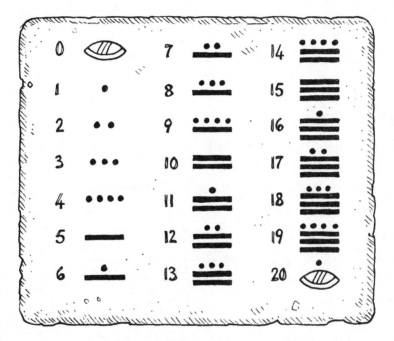

It's a really easy system to learn. The Aztecs were still using the bars and
dot numbers to count with hundreds of years later! The dot is one and the
dash is five. So three dots is three, two dashes are ten. A dot and three
dashes is sixteen and so on. The sign for '0' is a shell.

See if you can work out the following sums using the Mayan system.
But watch out for the trick questions!

1 • • is company but • • • is a crowd. So what is • • • • and ▬ ?

2 • stitch in time saves ●●●●/▬. So • • stitches will save how many?

3 If ••• sick Mayans need to munch on ▬•▬ bats' wings each to make themselves well, how many bats do they need to catch?

4 If a Mayan priest rips out •• hearts every weekday, ▬•▬ hearts on Saturday, and has a rest on Sunday, how many sacrifices will he have made in a week?

5 If a Mayan mother cuts off • finger every time one of her babies dies, how many fingers would she cut off if ≡≡≡ of her babies died?

Answers:
1 ••••▬ ; 2 •••≡ ; 3 ••••▬ ; 4 •≡≡ ; 5 ≡≡≡ .

Awful Aztecs

The Aztecs took a lot of their nasty habits from the Maya … and they invented some of their own.

When it came to human sacrifices, the Aztecs really did things on a big scale. The awful Aztecs sacrificed 50,000 people a year! (In fact for a really special occasion when they opened a new temple they sacrificed 20,000 people at a single party.) They had to have a special army just to find new victims for the busy priests and were happy to stir up trouble in conquered lands so they had an excuse to round up some more prisoners to sacrifice.

Try this quick quiz and find out how much you know about the awful Aztecs.

1 The Aztecs arrived in Central America and survived by eating something that was supposed to kill them! What? (Clue: they ate it and said, 'Fangs very much!')

2 The Aztecs took the religion of the Toltec people which said they had to worship what? (Clue: if they didn't worship it then the earth would go cold)

3 The Aztecs made human sacrifices to their gods by ripping out the live, beating hearts of their victims. Where did they do this? (Clue: the Egyptians had these too)

4 Ordinary Aztecs ate a few things we might find disgusting. What pet did they snack on? (Clue: hot _____?)

5 The human sacrifices were thrown off the altar after death. But the corpse wasn't all wasted. What happened to some of the bodies? (Clue: a tasteful way to treat a corpse)

6 In March, the priests didn't just sacrifice human victims, they skinned them. What did they do with the skins? (Clue: made a winter warmer?)

7 In April children would often be sacrificed. The Aztecs took them as close as they could to their sun god – even higher than their highest pyramid. Where? (Clue: did they stop and 'ave-a-rest?)

8 One thing the Aztec peasants had, but didn't eat, was chocolate. What did they use cocoa beans for? (Clue: it was a rich food)

9 What did Aztec boys do to their teeth to make them look fierce? (Clue: can you see the point of this?)

10 A dead Aztec child was buried. What did the Aztecs use instead of a coffin? (Clue: dead jammy!)

Answers:

1 Snakes. When the Aztecs arrived in Central America there were five tribes living there. These tribes said the only spare land was an island – but they knew the island was infested by snakes. The tribes thought they'd get rid of the Aztecs. But the Aztecs ate the snakes. Adder way to do it.

2 The sun. To the Aztecs the sun wasn't a ball of fiery gas – it was a god and that god needed constant sacrifices to keep going.

3 On pyramids. But the Aztec pyramids weren't tombs, they were temples. They sacrificed victims on the top – as near to their sun god as they could get.

4 Dog. They also ate frogs and tadpoles, lizards, ants, toads, monkeys and cacti. Scrummy!

5 The Aztecs ate them. Not the whole body, just slices of the leanest leg perhaps. And it was only the priests who had this cannibal treat.

6 Made them into cloaks. The priests wore them for twenty (smelly, sticky) days.

7 The mountains. The children were usually slave children. After all, the Aztecs couldn't go on too long sacrificing their own children or there'd be none left!

8 Money. The rich people drank hot chocolate made from ground cocoa with vanilla and honey – but this was a luxury and the precious cocoa beans were used as money by the poorer people. Imagine yourself eating a five-pound-note sandwich and you'll understand why the poor didn't eat chocolate!

9 They filed them to a point. Of course this would help them tear the flesh off that dog they were eating. But don't try this at home, boys.

10 A jar. Not a glass jamjar, of course, but a pottery jar. Not a lot of fun being an Aztec child – if your parents were too poor to keep you they could sell you as a slave.

Weird wedding

Fancy getting married the good old Aztec way? Imagine you are an Aztec boy. See if you can work out which of these marriage customs are true and which are false.

1 When you've chosen your bride, you need to send your dad over with a marriage proposal.

2 You should propose to the girl's family.

3 You must also get permission from your teacher so you can get married.

4 All Aztecs get married on the same day, so don't worry about picking a wedding date.

5 You need to arrange a feast before the wedding.

6 The bride is carried to your house for the wedding on the back of an old woman.

7 The wedding guests ride from the feast to the wedding on llamas.

8 Just before the wedding everyone gives you a wedding present.

9 You are joined together in marriage when your cloak is tied to your bride's blouse.

10 After the wedding there is a final feast where everyone can drink alcohol except the newly-weds.

Answers:

1 False. Your proposal must be given by an old woman. (Better wake up Granny!)

2 True. Don't bother asking the girl herself – you don't need her permission to marry her!

3 True. Without teacher's permission the wedding is off.

4 False. You can chose your wedding day, but you've got to check your horoscopes and make sure it's a 'good' day on the Aztec calendar.

5 False. The girl's family organizes a feast at her house. The bride can sort out her make-up and wedding dress while the guests are eating. After the feast you must wait until dark because weddings take place at night.

6 True. Has to be a strong old lady!

7 False. Guests walk in a torch-lit procession to your house for the wedding.

8 True. The presents are given to the happy couple, who sit by the fire on a spread-out mat.
9 True. They really tie the knot!
10 False. Only guests over the age of 30 can drink alcohol.

Frightening fighters

Could you have made an awful Aztec warrior? Here are a few foul facts about the ferocious Aztec fighters – but you have to fit in the missing words.

1 AZTEC BOYS WERE GIVEN A MINI LOINCLOTH, SHIELD, CLOAK AND FOUR _____ WHEN THEY WERE A FEW DAYS OLD.

2 ALL AZTEC BOYS WENT TO SCHOOL AT 15 AND COULD CHOOSE TO BE TRAINED AS WARRIORS OR AS _____.

3 YOUNG MEN COULD BE MADE FULL WARRIORS BY HAVING THEIR FACES SMEARED WITH THE BLOOD OF A _____ THAT WAS STILL BEATING.

4 AZTEC WARRIORS WORE PADDED COTTON 'ARMOUR', WHICH WAS SOAKED IN _____ TO MAKE IT HARD.

5 THE AZTECS WERE ARMED WITH POWERFUL WOODEN CLUBS, EDGED WITH STONE _____.

6 RICH AZTEC WARRIORS WORE _____ THAT THEY BELIEVED HAD MAGICAL POWERS TO PROTECT THEM IN BATTLE.

7 WARRIORS SHORT OF FOOD WOULD EAT DEAD ENEMIES BUT WOULD NEVER EAT DEAD _____.

8 THE AZTEC ARMY NEEDED TO CAPTURE AT LEAST 20 _____ FOR SACRIFICE.

9 AZTEC WARRIORS BELIEVED IF THEY DIED IN BATTLE THEY WOULD TURN INTO _____ AND GO TO HEAVEN.

10 AZTEC LEADERS WORE LARGE STRUCTURES MADE OF _____ AND REEDS ON THEIR SHOULDERS.

Missing words, not in the correct order: salt water, feather, humming birds, precious stones, priests, arrows, enemy fighters, heart, blades, friends

Answers:
1 arrows; **2** priests; **3** heart; **4** salt water; **5** blades; **6** precious stones; **7** friends; **8** enemy fighters; **9** humming birds; **10** feathers.

DON'T YOU THINK THAT'S A LITTLE... WELL... TOO MUCH?

Savage Spanish

Of course, when the Spanish arrived in the 1520s the Aztecs suffered pretty horribly too! The Spanish used steel swords and guns against the Aztecs' wooden clubs and they quickly crushed the cruel Aztecs. But they were still afraid of Aztec rebellions. The Aztecs offered to entertain the Spanish conquerors with a dance. The soldiers heard a rumour that the Aztecs planned to kill them straight after the dance ... so the soldiers struck first. An Indian wrote this report ... but some of the words have been scrambled. Can you decode the dreadful deeds?

> They ran in among the dancers and attacked the man who was drumming and cut off his MARS. They cut off his DEAH and it DROLLE across the ROLFO. Then they attacked the dancers, stabbing them, SPAREING them and striking some with their DROWSS. They attacked some from behind and these fell instantly to the ground with their STUG hanging out. Some attempted to run away but their STININSTEE dragged as they ran; they seemed to tangle their TEEF in their own entrails. Others they beheaded; they cut off their heads or PILTS their heads to pieces. No matter how they tried to save themselves, they could find no escape.

Answers:
These are the unscrambled words in the correct order: arms, head, rolled, floor, spearing, swords, guts, intestines, feet, split

Quick Aztecs quiz

See if you can guess the answers to this quick quiz about the angry Aztecs.

1 The Aztecs had little wooden huts on the side of the road in both the country and the town. Aztecs popped in for a couple of minutes before coming out again looking content. What were the little wooden huts?
a) shrines to Aztec gods
b) public toilets
c) pubs for drinking maize wine

2 What sort of knife did the priests use to cut out a victim's heart?
a) glass
b) stone
c) gold

3 Aztecs were told what to wear. Poor people wore simple clothing and lords wore rich clothing. What was the punishment for a poor person caught wearing rich clothes for a second time?
a) death
b) slavery
c) having their house knocked down

4 The Aztec traders became very rich and dressed in fine clothes. But the emperor wouldn't let them do this in public. So what did they do?
a) hid their fine clothes under plain ankle-length cloaks
b) wore reversible coats – rich outside but plain inside so they could flip it over if the emperor was around
c) crept into the city at night so no one could see them

5 Aztec children were given the job of collecting things in the fields. What did they collect?
a) berries
b) beetles
c) bat droppings

6 Before the Aztecs came the Olmecs. The Olmecs were known as what?
a) the rubber people
b) the green monkey people
c) the cactus-haired people

7 How did Aztecs keep their teeth clean?
a) with toothpicks made from cactus spines
b) by using chewing gum
c) with toothpaste from powdered beetles

8 Aztecs used to gather the green scum from the edge of a lake. Why?
a) to use it as a medicine
b) to dye their clothes with it
c) to eat it

9 When subjects were leaving the emperor what did they have to do?
a) crawl out on their hands and knees
b) walk out of the room backwards
c) bow seven times

10 The Aztec emperor would be offered a choice of how many dishes of food at each meal?
a) six
b) 42
c) 100

Answers:

1b) The Aztecs encouraged people to use public toilets. The toilets would be emptied on to the soil to make it richer with human 'manure'.

2a) The knives were made of a type of natural glass that came from hardened volcanic lava.

3a) A peasant who tried to be posh had their house knocked down the first time they were caught. If they were caught again they were executed!

4c) The richer the merchants became, the greater the feasts they had to give to the nobles. The merchants had to give rich presents to their guests and buy extra slaves to be sacrificed.

5b) These beetles were crushed and used to make red dye for clothes. The Aztecs needed 150,000 beetles to make one kilo of dye!

6a) They got their name because they lived in the area where rubber trees grew.

7b) Aztecs chewed chicle gum made from a milky fluid inside some trees and plants.

8c) They pressed it into scrummy scummy cakes.

9b) Everyone had to bow their heads to the emperor and no one was allowed to turn their back on him.

10c) The emperor was shielded from ordinary people, eating behind a screen of gold.

EPILOGUE

You've read the book, so now you can take one final test. If you can get these ten brain-teasing questions right, you are truly an ancient brainbox. Award yourself a cardboard medal and a Roman party – a few dormouse sandwiches with fish-gut sauce should do it. Just get these foul facts in the right order…

1. GREEK PLAYWRIGHT AESCHYLUS… SERVED GUESTS AT A FEAST WITH… WILD ELEPHANTS

2. A sick Mayan… escaped being killed by… honey

3. INJURED ROMAN GLADIATORS… LOOKED INTO THE FUTURE USING… A BATH

4. An Egyptian doctor… gave his corpse… snot and vomit

5. FRIENDS OF A DEAD GREEK… THREW AWAY… TOBACCO

6. Roman Emperor Eliogabalus… helped people by tasting… brains

7. A MESOPOTAMIAN FORTUNE TELLER… WOULD HAVE THEIR HEADS SMASHED WITH… 600 OSTRICH BRAINS

8. King Thutmose of Egypt… cured burns with… sheep guts

9. GREEK DOCTOR HIPPOCRATES… DIED WHEN HIT ON THE HEAD BY… A HAMMER

10. Mummy-makers in Egypt… would cure a snake bite by smoking… a tortoise

Answers:

1 Greek playwright Aeschylus died when hit on the head by a tortoise.

2 A sick Mayan would cure a snake bite by smoking tobacco.

3 Injured Roman gladiators would have their heads smashed with a hammer.

4 An Egyptian doctor cured burns with honey.

5 Friends of a dead Greek gave his corpse a bath.

6 Roman Emperor Eliogabalus served guests at a feast with 600 ostrich brains.

7 A Mesopotamian fortune-teller looked into the future using sheep guts.

8 King Thutmose of Egypt escaped being killed by wild elephants.

9 Greek doctor Hippocrates helped people by tasting snot and vomit.

10 Mummy-makers in Egypt threw away brains.

So there you have it! Just a quick look at the vomit-tasting Greek doctors, cannibal Aztec priests, murdering mad Roman emperors, and evil Egyptian grave-robbers.

Here we are in the 21st century. Of all the amazing facts there is one amazing-most fact of all … that we humans have survived this long! How on earth did we manage it?

Now why not visit www.terry-deary.com